# IDENTIFICATION AND INDIVIDUALITY

## *Instincts Fundamental to Human Behavior*

**JOHN T. FLYNN, M.D.**

*Chief of Medicine*
*The Beekman-Downtown Hospital*

Former Chief Psychiatrist
56th U.S. Army General Hospital

*Monograph Series*

SECOND EDITION

THE
BEEKMAN PRESS
NEW YORK
1970

BEEKMAN PRESS
170 William Street
New York, N.Y. 10038

Printed in U.S.A.

Library of Congress Catalog Card Number 77-130955

To all

who helped

and

guided me

"The lights were very bright and there were four or five mirrors all around me. And as I looked at myself, all I could see clearly was my mother looking at me—my own dead mother, stooped a little and everything.

And I resented it and wanted to fight against it."

H.N.
January 1951

# Contents

# *Preface to the 2nd Edition*

In an earlier presentation of these views, I abandoned the ambition of a detailed account and confined myself to a statement of general experience and of proposed principles. The favorable response of interested readers has encouraged me to believe that an amplified restatement of my thesis would receive equal consideration.

In prefacing this slightly larger volume, I wish to re-emphasize an earlier concern that generalizations in psychology and psychiatry too often seem to rest upon maximum interpretation of minimum data. 20th Century psychology and psychiatry are still in that observational stage which characterizes the bulk of modern astronomy — one can observe but must be cautious as to conclusions, one can record changes but very often be uncertain as to underlying mechanisms. From the vantage of this view, one's humility need not be further encouraged.

At the end of 4000 hours, I set down some 98,000 items of behavior on a total of 140 patients, at which point the truth was clearly evident, i.e., a blind statistical listing would be mere empty tabulation unless I first extracted carefully certain basic facts about these experiences.

Careful reflection upon these hours of patient-experience clearly indicated that:

1. People have "problems" — reflected by their persistence in searching for alternative "solutions".

2. Such a problem may be a conflict with the environs or it may be internal within the subject.

3. A single problem may have both internal and external aspects.

4. External conflicts or the external aspect of a problem appear easier for the subject to discuss, though often he may fail to recount the details correctly.

5. An internal conflict or the internal aspects of a problem are more difficult for the subject to admit or discuss, and they may even be denied; but their presence, if not their character, can be detected by a simple cross check — how and to what extent does the subject's outward behavior contradict his expressed intentions and apparent convictions? A persistent discrepancy of this kind must reflect internal forces which are actively at cross purposes to one another.

So — people have problems which have internal and external aspects. Before we dismiss this statement as hardly earth-shaking, let us see what questions flow from it.

1. Is there a consistently found external aspect of these conflicts? If patients' words, endlessly repeated, are to be believed, their major conflicts center upon *other people*— and not upon any casual or remote persons but upon people who are closest to them: wife, husband, children, parents, close relatives, in-laws, lovers, mistresses, boss, subordinates, i.e., their identificands.

2. What can be consistently stated about the internal aspect of such conflicts? Again from patients' description and behavior, it appears that such internal conflicts or internal aspects of conflict can be life-long and yet be compatible with good overall human function. Indeed the impression is inescapable that a very large measure of such internal conflict is *normal,* varying in degree and in expression from one phase of life to the next, but normal nevertheless. If this impression is true, then an internal disagreement or struggle must take place between two or more *separate* forces (which for lack of a better designation we will call instincts), for it is impossible to believe that an internal conflict could exist on the basis of internal inconsistencies within *one* internal force or instinct. Nature does not create forces which are inconsistent within themselves; or if She does, the bearers of such forces do not long maintain their integrity. By contrast, two separate instincts, intended for the sustaining of

the individual or of the species, can maintain a life-long conflict and yet not interfere with the "normal" development and maturation of the individual.

By the logic of this thesis it is not possible that a single instinct, such as the sexual instinct, *by itself* can form the basis of a majority of human internal conflict. If we must assume that the sexual instinct cannot be in conflict with itself, then its role in human conflict must depend upon its antagonisms toward other and equally powerful instincts.

On the basis of experience and reflection, I was persuaded that human conflict relates directly and most importantly to other people who are close to the subject: that within the subject are instinctual forces which are consistent within themselves but often in conflict with one another, to both normal and abnormal degrees. The remainder of this book is devoted to an application of the above premises to a wide spectrum of human behavior.

# Prologue

Despite the rapid expansion of scientific understanding during the 20th century, we remain without a satisfactory theory of individual and collective human behavior[1]. Psychoanalytic theory has emphasized those aspects of human behavior most closely related to the sexual instinct. It has not viewed sex within the larger framework of human instincts. For many years the author has been persistently dissatisfied with the involved and highly symbolized psychoanalytic view, and has believed that human behavior can be understood from a less complicated yet fundamentally sound viewpoint.

The theory here presented is based on a ten year study which reflects the author's experience as a military psychiatrist, as a special research fellow in internal medicine and psychiatry, and as an active practitioner. In addition to many hundreds of general observations, four thousand clinical hours were specially devoted to close study of 140 patients chosen from clinic and private practice.

Certain fundamental premises, derived from these experiences, have consistently supplied a reasonable basis of understanding in many areas of human behavior. These premises originate from the operation of two distinct yet inseparable instinctual forces—*identification* and *individuality;* and can be stated as follows:

1) Human behavior reflects basic human instincts.

2) Human behavior is dominated by the growth and operation of two antagonistic but cooperating instincts—the need for identification and the drive toward individuality.

3) The instinct for identification is the inner need to establish unity or combination with one or more other human beings (identificands).[2] Things and places may also have identification values.

1

4) The instinct for individuality is the inner drive to establish one's self as a separate unique entity independently capable of self-assertion.

5) Because of the opposing character of their aims, the instincts for identification and individuality maintain a life-long antagonism, accounting for the multiform confusion and frequent contradictions of behavior in the normal human being. It is the eventual progressive cooperative adaption of these two instincts which produces the quality of maturity in adult human beings.

6) Instincts "grow" in the sense that each successive stage of life requires, and should produce, a progressively more sophisticated level of instinct function. Human conduct is "normal" when it is governed by normally developing instincts, even though the instincts are in conflict with one another.

7) The natural growth of instincts can be thwarted by a combination of forces the nature of which is not clear, but which seems to arise from constitutional, hereditary, and environmental conditions. Non-psychotic human conduct is "abnormal" when governed by inadequately developed instincts.

8) The sexual instinct is of major importance in the control of behavior and contributes to the quality of maturity, but sexual function is, as often as not, subject to the operation of the instincts of identification and individuality. Were this not so, social and personal chaos would follow.

The continued growth and interaction of the two major instinctual forces can produce numbers and complexities of phenomena beyond the observational capacity of a single individual, just as gravitation and inertia produce an endless profusion of motions in the physical world. The author, therefore, will emphasize concepts and examples rather than attempt a quantitation of data. Further evidence will develop from the reader's own experiences when he gives this theory his thoughtful attention, re-examines old ideas, and sees human life in fresh focus.

An important condition of instinct growth and function is its autonomy, i.e., its independence from control by the human being himself. At first glance this condition would seem to deny the possibility of "free will", self-determination, and personal responsibility in human behavior. The paradox dissolves if we agree that the drive to establish individuality and to maintain unique self-expression is a fundamental instinctual force which no one can totally thwart or suppress within himself. In fact, the steady struggle to maintain individuality against external forces and against the powerful need for identification is a major determinant of human behavior, giving to it the characteristics we call personal liberty and human freedom.

No attempt is made in this book to define or describe all human instincts, but attention is focussed mainly upon those instincts which seem to affect day-to-day behavior most importantly.

# Instinct Growth and Development

Fundamental to an understanding of the two major instincts is a review of their steady growth and interaction through successive stages of human life. Well established observations[3] illustrate the gradual development of these two instincts. What follows here is an overview of behavior from infancy through adulthood, with the unavoidable inaccuracies which are inevitable in any attempt at a comprehensive summary. The purpose is to illustrate the growth and development of these two instincts.

Though identification and individuality may at times be discussed separately they do in fact develop together in an inseparable and mutually helpful union, in spite of their natural antagonism.

## Identification

Identification is the instinct which involves "the placing of one's self in the situation of another person and assuming the characteristics of that person."[4] This working definition cannot encompass all the conditions and capacities of this instinct, but is a reasonable starting point. For example, comparative zoology studies of imprinting and following patterns in animals[5] suggest that at birth many species are highly susceptible to identifications through vision and hearing. The freshly hatched gosling identifies itself with the first object seen; if this object is other than the adult female of the species, confusion can result. When this first "identificand" is grossly inappropriate and the identification persists, the term "silly as a goose" is understandable.

Such ease of establishing identification is not obvious in the human at birth, though during the first weeks a primitive level of sucking and swallowing allows a steady incorporation of external objects into the organism; a close

4

relationship with outside objects is thus established. By sixteen weeks of age grasping activities with the hands begin
to cement this relationship further; there is even anticipa-
tion of feeding, bathing, and affection. The infant is incor-
porating into himself, and merging into, the patterns of
outside behavior which directly affect him. During the first
year the infant progresses through exploratory use of the
index finger for picking and poking, to the more complex
function of placing one object inside another,—an external
counterpart of incorporation which will later undergo enor-
mous refinement. Imitation of gestures and facial expressions becomes progressively more sophisticated. There is
greater discrimination between the familiar, with which
the infant is identified, and the unfamiliar The emergence
of emotional activity (fear, anger, affection, anxiety, jealousy) seems to be association with an empathy or awareness
of the same feelings in others.

During the second year the developing child seems to
grasp the notion of "united" and "separate", assembling
like objects and separating others into their diverse com-
ponents. The concept of ownership is grasped,—identification of an object with a person. Separation from persons
with whom the child is identified gives rise to emotional
display, indicating a thwarting or disturbance of instinct
function. By two years of age memory and recall show a
higher neurological development, along with more advanced incorporations and identifications. The child begins
to identify words with objects. Other clear-cut identifications are seen in youngsters of both sexes who act out the
parent-child relationship through playing with dolls and
"playing house". This typical play pattern clearly foreshadows a subtle but highly important facet of the identification function,—the ability to identify an outside person
with a second outside person or object. "Playing house" involves a whole complex of identifications,—self with parent,
self with doll, sibling with parent, doll with sibling, self

with sibling, self with nursemaid, play situation with real situation. This kind of multiple identification in later life will make human behavior seem endlessly complicated. In primitive societies simpler identifications of the same type can have catastrophic force, as illustrated by the sticking of pins into images.

By age five the child has shown an active need to conform, yet wants the outside to conform to him; this conflict is inherent in identification and individuality instinct function. He is, like his parents, protective toward younger children. He takes pride in his school and begins to play in a group, rather than in the previous solitary but parallel fashion. He is unsettled by disturbed social conditions because of the strength of his identification with those about him. Up to this age the most forceful identifications are with the parents, and are verbalized directly,—"just like", "just as tall as", etc. Later years see a gradual loosening of these bonds, but they are never completely broken.

We shall pause here to consider the development of the companion instinct of individuality during the first five years of life.

## Individuality

The instinct of individuality is the inborn striving for separateness and uniqueness. It determines the child's rebellions against parents and siblings, the negative resistance of the adolescent, the very human urge to resist any restraints on freedom and the creative expressive aspects of human behavior. In the first weeks of life individuality is not obviously discernible, though evidence for this has been offered elsewhere.[6] Very early, however, the infant begins to be self-assertive in his reactions to environmental pressures such as changes of schedule. Later, he begins to discern the individual characteristics of external objects. At age one there is no clear cut distinction between self and others, but six months later the use of "me" and "you" suggests some awareness of the difference. The infant's identification with outside patterns is so strong that when these patterns are disturbed his demand for their reinstatement is a loud and insistent personalized expression of individuality. This merging of function by the two instincts is seen more and more obviously as growth continues, even when the process is marked by their mutual antagonism. By two years the child begins to sense oneness versus multiplicity, and can distinguish his own image in a mirror from those of others. He tends toward solitary play, dawdles, and can be negativistic,—traits suggestive of a slowly organizing self-determination. At this age the temporary dominance of one instinct over the other, so important in adolescent and adult life, is already evident. By three years the child seems aware, in a fragmentary fashion, that he is one person and that you, the outsider, are another; yet he becomes angry at inanimate objects as if they were people, and talks to himself as to another person. Four years of age is self-assertive, bossy, verbal, and creative; the first person pronoun fills his speech. Five settles down to a foreshadowing of the mature adult in whom the forces of identification and individuality have accomplished a working truce. He is calmly self-dependent, serious, anxious to excel, yet friendly, and well identified with his parents, playmates, and possessions.

## Further Development of Identification and Individuality

From this point it is sensible to follow the two developing instincts together. The disturbances which accompany any shifting of identifications, the apparent ascendancy of one instinct over the other at times, and the signs of their progressive cooperation toward maturity will be discussed.

Six is a good age at which to observe the temporary ascendancy of the instinct for individuality. The child is often extremely individualistic,—brash, at war with the world, demanding, contradictory in his expression of love (identification) and hate (rejection of identification by individuality). At the same time he is most susceptible to charms and symbols which later will have more identification value. Age six, perhaps, foreshadows adolescence.

Seven reveals long periods of calm, self-absorption, shyness and brooding, suggesting an inner effort to consolidate new identifications. There are new attachments to father, teacher, friends; resistance against maternal dominance is better organized. An outstanding characteristic is the tendency to be a "model child" when away from home, yet a source of resistance and turbulence at home. This is a normal condition wherein the instinct for individuality asserts itself in the presence of the identificands (parents, siblings); in their physical absence the instinct for individuality has less need to assert itself and allows the identification instinct to function. The fact that strong identifications are most effective when the person is not in the physical presence of the identificand will be observed throughout later life.

Eight begins to turn more actively to the outside world. He watches and learns from adults, is affectionate and demands affection. He likes to be with his parents now that other identifications with teachers and friends are established. He has a better sense of his own status, can shift his attention from one identification to another, and shows less aggressive need to protect his individuality at all times.

Nine has progressed further, with some critical capacity toward self as well as others, without great turmoil, yet with evident self-preoccupation. Conscience is clearly in the making, with a more orderly arrangement of principles incorporated from heredity and environment, and reinforced by identification with the source of these principles,—ancestors, parents, playmates, siblings, religion, heroes of the worlds of history, sports, and art.

Ten progresses still further into the adult world with a well defined individuality of desires, tastes, and talents. At the same time he identifies more easily with broadening ideas and prejudices. Group, club or gang identification takes precedence over that with the family. Group life is now organized, with serious secret symbolisms and austerities. Comradeship is preferred to competition, though the ten year old is subject to occasional outbursts of anger and violence, especially against siblings where a close identification can arouse individualistic rebellion. Against the outside world, however, loyalty to siblings is unquestioned.

Eleven is an adolescent in the making. There is greater self-assertion, curiosity, competitiveness, and vigorous physical activity; extremes of emotion move him from rage to laughter. He shows increased sociability and dislikes being alone; he identifies with others of his age who are seeking self-assertive accomplishment. Again, he is the model child away from home, yet difficult and rude with his parents. His ability to work well with one group against another, even at this unstable period, is evidence of the cooperation of the two instincts.

Twelve is again a period of greater calm, the child being more reasonable and companionable. Feelings are held under better control. Mother-daughter relationships may improve. Simultaneously, although the child is able to take the initiative, the group viewpoint assumes great importance. Boys tend toward large groups; girls attach themselves to small groups. Neither yet shows attachment to the opposite sex. For the boy this period is strongly colored by identification with sports or military heroes and even with some form of authority resting in part on superior force.

The teenager period ushers in an upheaval of identifications, coincident with a vigorous upsurge of individuality. The egocentric, apparently indifferent, demanding, rebellious adolescent begins to reject many identifications of childhood, especially the powerful identification with his parents. He can view his parents more objectively and express criticism of them openly; his criticism of them is no longer an act of self-criticism through identification. As a result of such weakened identification, and with no new stable identifications established, the adolescent remains unsure, restless, moving constantly through a series of brief identifications with new figures, close and distant. In retrospect, childhood is thought of as happy and secure; the old identifications upon which that security was based are losing their vigor and value.

Thirteen is withdrawn, worried, and feels strange in his new found sense of individual aloneness. The physical changes and new sensations of sexual development add to the unsettled state. He is apt to be shy, moody, antagonistic, and markedly sensitive to criticism. Correspondingly, this inner awareness appears to enhance awareness of others; there is a heightened sensitivity to new identifications. He is loyal to his group in a more passive fashion than previously. He seeks to improve younger siblings and gets on well with them, as though assuming some of the parental role. When uncomfortable with himself he may take on an imaginary role and be someone else. There is an intense interest in movies, T.V., sports, and literature in the search for new personalities with whom to identify.

Fourteen is more confident and communicative, still critical of parents but less tense in the relationship. Individuality is more comfortable; identifications are still shifting but seem, for the moment, to cause less discomfort. Attachment to a group is counterbalanced by interest in one's own traits and characteristics. Still, there is little mingling of the sexes. Boys remain interested in sports and group activity. Girls already share their interest in marriage and it is frequently the subject of endless tireless communication among them. The girl identifies with her eventual wife-mother role early, the boy much later with his creative work role.

Fifteen often represents a brief period of difficulty in most spheres. He is indifferent, lazy, frequently lacks interest in food, and is generally apathetic. There is a confused awareness of self,—an attempt to be precise and perfection-istic without knowing precisely how this will add to his individuality. Feelings of resentment are mirrored in the desire to be away from home and out of contact with his family. There may be cultivation of a deep friendship with another boy his age, a situation often described as homo-sexual, perhaps more in feeling state than physical action. There may be brief periods of strong need for physical affec-tion from the parent of the opposite sex. There are clear cut sexual factors in this situation but it has also the charac-ter of a trying-out phase, as though beginning to identify with the marital role appropriate for later life. For the first time the adolescent may be thinking of himself *primarily* in terms of his own life, home, marriage, occupation, and personal success.

Sixteen is at the threshold of adulthood. He has greater self possession and self reliance; there is a calmer acceptance of changed identifications and confidence in the ability to establish new and stable ones. With the sense of independ-ence comes greater resistance to mob influence, the ability to discriminate between good and bad identifications, and a greater tolerance toward the world, though not toward its injustices. There is a willingness to scatter identifications and be content with ones of brief duration. Sixteen has less time for the family, but friends are brought into the family circle and there is a generally better relationship. Self awareness has diminished, though independence remains strong; there is a greater willingness to see another's point of view. An intense interest in the opposite sex reflects the ultimate orientation of the sexual instinct. This opens new avenues of growth as well as conflict.

The adolescent passes through one or a series of "puppy-love" affairs that give rise to great amusement for adults. Such affairs are extremely useful in freeing the adolescent from old and strong identifications with the parent of the opposite sex. These new attachments—brief, idealized, violent—are rarely stable because they are a reliving of *old* identifications, without consideration for the individuality instinct. The latter repeatedly blunts the force of these "infatuation" identifications, yet such episodes are highly important to the maturation of the identification instinct. By means of them the adolescent loosens the grip of parental identification and otherwise would not make a suitable adult identification with spouse and children. This loosening is accompanied by emotional turmoil, a condition that marks the forming or breaking of important identifications throughout life.

Once such "infatuations" are lived through and discarded, the young adult normally moves on to a freer choice of "steady girl" or "boy friend" and eventually a marital partner. During the marital years the identification instinct is manifested in a strong love-identification with spouse and offspring. This is usually a time of relatively stable relationship with parents who are now regarded, at best, as friends stripped of much but by no means all of their identification value. It is also however a time when previously unrecognized identification problems may well come to light. The most obvious one—antagonism between mother-in-law and son-in-law—is so universal that it must be considered normal. It is difficult to clarify this mutual rejection, but two thoughts are worthy of speculation. The mother loses a strong identificand when her daughter turns away toward a marital partner. Further, due to increasing age, loss of fertility, and diminishing domestic importance it is a time of generally unsettled identification and individuality demands for the mother. It is natural that the son-in-law, who apparently hastens this process and causes her decrease in importance, should be resented. The son-in-law, on the other hand, no doubt harbors some resentment of his own mother's dominance in his early life; the new threat is recognized immediately by the male individuality. Under such circumstances, if close connections between older and younger generations are maintained, the possibility of discord is great—another evidence of the rebellion of individuality against too tightly bound identifications.*

In our culture the forging of a new family unit usually involves the establishment of a separate domicile. This milieu is the major locale and focus for the wife; the husband reinforces his identification through financial commitment and physical labor about the home.**

Procreation brings the sexual instinct into close cooperation with the instincts of identification and individuality. The fulfillment of sexual drive involves a union of one person with another. This identification is accomplished in a variety of ways. Besides the act of physical union, the individuality needs for dominance and submission, for pleasure and possession are satisfied. Beyond these momentary satisfactions there is the more enduring one of reproduction, a function in which there is such full play of identification and individuality that no adequate listing is possible. In particular, the moment of childbirth has special significance; when physical incorporation of the infant is relinquished at its birth, there occurs an abrupt and dramatic identification with the new born infant for both parents, especially for the new mother. The surge of mother instinct at first sight, sound, and touch of the baby ensures its physical well being as a matter of course. At no other time of life are the instincts for identification and individuality so well merged and so completely fulfilled. The mother and father view childbirth as a unique and creative accomplishment; their appraisal customarily overlooks their role as passive vehicles of natural forces.

Many other satisfactions of these two instincts are sought by the parents during the early years of child rearing. One

---

*Within specific families there may be variations, i.e., mother v. daughter-in-law, father v. son-in-law, etc.

**In this connection it is interesting to note that old identifications with place may prevail; the new family often lives in the "old block", near the "old school", etc. Identification with place can be exceptionally strong, especially under circumstances of bitter hardship and shared deprivation.

may take the form of deciding that the struggles of one's own youth shall not be the lot of the offspring. The parent who makes this the major focus of his relationship with a child often meets complete defeat. Intensified concern in a parent with a problem of the past indicates that there has been a failure to resolve it. The growing child who naturally identifies so closely with the parent, will take the same problem into himself. A specific problem can thus pass from generation to generation, though most commonly with lessening force.

Identification and individuality in the parent find outlet in ambitions for the child's success, a desire that the latter's accomplishments surpass those of the parents. By identifying with a child's successes the parent expands his own, especially if he feels that he was responsible for guiding the child toward unusually productive effort. In the offspring's early years, when barely discernible physical similarities to a parent are enthusiastically discussed and exaggerated, there may exist the opposite situation,—the child may develop traits of the parent which the latter has rejected in himself; it may experience a distressing phase of growth previously experienced by the parent. Such traits and tendencies in the child are little altered by anxious discipline or punishment by the parent; they may be enhanced when the child identifies strongly with the parent.

Normally, once parental identification with a child is set in motion, it continues throughout life. There are suitable modifications, but the parental need to find personal extension through the child remains its essence. Aims, ambitions, and successes of the child become the parent's. Conversely, the force of failure is felt more deeply. The force of such an identification is somewhat dissipated when there are several children.

The occupational career of a human being requires special comment. In the male, career-choice with often intense identification with that creative life work is the end

result of a working out of strong individuality needs which
find expression in the work itself or in the leisure that work
makes possible.[7] Tempering such choice, however, are well
established identifications with the parent's cultural-educa-
tional ideals, locale, group mores, and the pattern of domes-
tic-marital attachments. This important choice of life work
and goals, a so-called "identity crisis", illustrates the proper
cooperation between identification and individuality instincts in establishing a mature life pattern. The period of
striving toward establishment of this goal is usually the
latter part of adolescence in the male, but does not find a
counterpart in the female until the latter reaches the middle
of the fourth decade. The pattern of female life work is
most often set by the natural phenomena of child-bearing
and motherhood; no choice of an external career need be
made until the most important female values (child-bearing, child rearing, and attractiveness of physical appearance) begin to wane late in the fourth decade.[8]

During the early adult years the male finds that the
instincts of identification and individuality are constantly
operative in the area of career or job interest. Older successful men are imitated. Factory group, company "family", or
military unit offer a continuance of family identification.
Outbursts of the individuality instinct are reflected in resentment at direction by others and "griping". A few young
adults will have such urgent individuality needs, coupled
with natural talent, that they will either bypass the group
or forge ahead to its leadership. Occasionally this instinct
may so predominate that it fosters a career effort largely
separated from other people, with ruthless disregard for
the experience of elders. Often such a career leads to discovery and new knowledge; more often there are slips and
stumbles until the individual's own experience begins to
broaden and support him.

During the fourth decade of life the individuality instinct
in both male and female becomes more insistent. A group

relationship in business or professional life is often dropped in favor of individual effort. Where there is little opportunity to find satisfaction in this area, individuality outlets may be shifted to non-occupational interests such as vacations and "time-off". At the same time, other and severe disturbances are taking place in the identification and individuality patterns. This is more especially true for women whose instincts up to this time have operated in the narrower area of the home.

The wife who submerged herself in a happy identification with husband and children awakens to a changing world. Children are older and increasingly assertive of their own individuality needs; they are beginning to leave home and thus diminish the importance of her role. The marital partner is examined more critically and found wanting. The wife's own ambitions, so long merged with his, find frustration in his failures. His preoccupation with work is no longer viewed as a combined effort between them but as a theft of attention and possible loss of interest in her. Personal looks, taken for granted, are beginning to fade, forcing a change in the picture of her own identity and individuality. Finally, the pillars of the past are crumbling,— older identificands, such as parents, are becoming feeble and dependent. A most of identifications comes under reexamination,—many are found wanting, yet there appear to be few new ones to replace them. Such turmoil usually appears in women shortly after the age of thirty-five; later, the menopause will add its own burdens. This phenomenon has been called the "disease without a name" or the "feminine mystique". This upsurge of individuality often forces into the open a vociferous rebellion against those closest to the woman; and against those values by which she formerly set great store. Often, the rebellion is secret, hidden away along with the whiskey bottles and tranquillizers.

For the man, the "dangerous age" of forty opens up similar awarenesses conditioned by his success or failure in attaining the goals with which he has identified so long, and which he feels are the mark of his individuality.

This is the period of a most realistic appraisal of life, based more on experience than on the earlier uncontrolled need of adolescence to assert individuality. It is conditioned by the awareness that life will not continue indefinitely,—that the remaining years must be spent in satisfying unfulfilled individuality needs, and that acceding to the needs of others with whom one is identified is no longer as satisfying as it once was.

Responses to the new instinct developments vary widely. If a marriage has been based on too strong an identification of one's marital partner with one's parent, the relationship is now found irksome by the restless individuality needs. In most families it is too late, because of children, financial considerations, inertia, and even some affection for the spouse, to consider a permanent change. Most couples struggle through this period with no attempt at change. Others try extramarital affairs, alcohol, or the psychiatrist's couch. Where the choice of a marital partner was originally made after the disappearance of the "infatuation"-identifications of adolescence, a marriage will be more inclined to survive this period of "delayed adolescence" in the fourth and fifth decades of life.

The forties are also plagued by physical change that adds to these problems. "Change of life" is more emphatically climaxed for the woman by its attendant loss of fertility. However, the female's identification with reproduction and her individuality satisfactions derived from it have already lessened in any event. Despite the fact that she may even welcome a cessation of the reproductive years this time is often accompanied by a strong feeling of loss, self pity and suffering not based upon any corresponding severity of physical symptoms. The reasons for this are not entirely clear, but these symptoms often occur markedly in a woman who suddenly finds herself passing through a phase of life similar to one in which she had observed her own mother. The woman had earlier regarded her mother's menopausal complaints with scorn, contempt, and fear, but now finds herself strongly identified with the mother's menopausal situation and undergoes the same anxieties and suffering.

The male climacteric is a parallel situation wherein the male individuality may sustain the blow of decreased sexual potency. At this time he may also experience depression and anxiety in the face of limited accomplishment short of goals set by his individuality instinct earlier in life.

Thus the late fourth and early fifth decades of life are periods of reorientation of individuality instinct drives as well as less marked shifts in identifications. To most people it is apparent that drastic action such as divorce and a new career is simply not practical. Expediency, however, may be brushed aside in favor of middle-aged divorce and re-marriage, or shift of occupational effort.

Identification-individuality patterns continue to change in later life, but not dramatically. The late fifth and sixth decades appear relatively stable. For the male, however, the time of occupational retirement may be as disrupting, in its way, as was the earlier loss of maternal importance for the female. Such abrupt cut-off can mean disaster, especial-ly where strikingly successful occupational achievement re-sulted from strong identification-individuality drives. Alter-natives to disastrous retirement must involve a carefully planned shift of instinctual outlets through new pursuits,— hobbies for which there is now time, reduced activity in one's old business, or the rare transfer to a new and less demanding occupation.

At this time of life certain old identifications, involving parents especially, must be relinquished. The identification-instinct reactions to the death of an identificand are so numerous and important that they will be discussed sepa-rately below. Most commonly, the death of a very aged parent is accepted as a normal event, with sufficient grief to allow a working through of the normal identification. This particular grief experience may not be so difficult because the survivors do not, in most instances in late middle life, require a replacement identification. The case may be quite different if a marital partner dies. Here the sense of identification, well established, has kept a couple together well beyond the years of physical attractiveness; the passionate driving incorporation has given way to a gentler affectionate companionship. In this situation, the death of one marital partner is often followed by the progressive debilitation and death of the other. Two casual factors must be operative here,—physical grief reactions may be withstood poorly by the aging organism, and the survivor may have a strong identification need to be united in death with the deceased.

With advancing years, identification with some phase of the character, illness or death of an old friend also occurs frequently. This is one of the outstanding features of mourning, but is reflected also in smaller ways,—an avid interest in obituary columns, long and detailed discussion of an illness, frequent attendance at funerals, morbid gossip, prediction of catastrophic events, and an increased interest in religion. This whole orientation seems to preface preparation for the final dissolution of the physical entity.

At every age, normal grief has certain characteristics which establish it as a normal phenomenon accompanying the death of a close identification.[9] The survivor passes through a period of rejection of the idea of permanent separation. The life like preservation of the embalmed corpse in every day clothes, the public viewing, chatting, even drinking and revelry that may extend to propping the corpse upright in a corner of the room are efforts to continue the identification as though the deceased were still alive. These activities are paralleled by others indicative of the broken identification,—the kneeling at wakes, the tolling of bells, the solemnity of the funeral. These events are followed and reinforced by a general feeling of depression, weeping, and withdrawal from active affairs for a brief period. Even after the initial intellectual acceptance of the fact of death there is the continued habit of speaking of the deceased in the present tense; the survivor must remind himself frequently that the person is no longer in existence. This inability to accept the fact of death may persist for several months. Eventually the survivor may be suddenly conscious of the fact, with emotional shock but acceptance. Others may struggle more fiercely to maintain the identification,—personal effects of the deceased are preserved intact; there may be seances with mediums to reestablish direct contact with the dead; mannerisms, habits of speech, and even clothing of the deceased may be adopted. Frequently there is a need to identify a living relative with the deceased as though the original identification had not been interrupted.* These particular features of grief have a most important bearing on many clinical problems faced by the physician, and will be illustrated in many of their various forms. Such features characterize grief at all ages, but are seen most commonly in the middle and later years when the death of identificands will most commonly occur.

Old age is most generally a time of looking back rather than forward. New identifications, like new habits, are not easily formed and so the old ones are relived. The aged person tends to identify with his younger self as though with another person. Yet individuality often finds even fuller expression in old age when the candid remark, disregard of rules, and dominance over social situations are most casually accepted by younger age groups. Lively individuality is more easily tolerated in the aged than at any other time of life because it carries with it much less threat of a true domination of the individuality of others.

It is said that the very old may welcome death as a

*"The king is dead; long live the king".

friend, as a reunion with the Great Majority. The need for old identifications lost through earlier deaths of identificands can be met only by one's own act of dying. This is in sharp contrast to the eager young years when identifications were constantly in the making and death was hardly given a passing thought.

# Some Special Features of Instinct Operation

In the cooperative-antagonistic development of the instincts of individuality and identification certain phenomena are observed to recur again and again. The first of these is the tendency of one instinct to demand intense satisfaction as though at the expense of the other. A careful study, however, reveals that the apparently less dominant instinct inevitably will find new and subtle ways to reinforce its position. Thus, during early adolescence the surface manifestation is rebellion against old identifications with a demanding surge of individuality; closer examination uncovers the fact that the very youthful individuality instinct finds itself extremely uncertain of its creative expression and needs to combine with the identification instinct in search of new identificands,—sports heroes, rock and roll singers, young teachers who become substitute expressions of individuality. The effort to reject parental identification is strong, sometimes violent, yet the individuality instinct cannot find sufficient strength to make such rejections complete. Apparent excesses of individuality may prove to be strikingly similar to the excesses of the parent, e.g., the extreme case of the illegitimate daughter herself having an illegitimate child.

Very often there is a special condition which forces one instinct to operate overtly; in the absence of that condition the instinct will function more normally. The most frequently observed "special" condition is the situation in which the child is openly rebellious in the physical presence of the parent. When the parent is not present the child automatically falls into the pattern of behavior set by the parent. The opposite kinds of response in the child can be recognized as clearly unhealthy. Model behavior when with the parent, and incorrigibility when away from him indicates poor strength of the individuality instinct unsupported by normal identification. Outward evidence of sibling rivalry appears most acutely in the physical presence of the parents; the identification of one sibling with another is blunted by the physical presence of the parents, but is reinforced by the aggressive action of an outsider toward one or both siblings.

Another special feature of these instincts are their relatively long periods of slow growth interspersed with considerable advances toward maturity. Childhood is marked by a series of important but not drastic alternations of instinct dominance. Unusual circumstances, such as the death or divorce of parents, or serious catastrophe in the surrounding world may cause upheaval of identifications. Even so, general comment in such circumstances often emphasizes "how well" the child accepted the disaster. The child, however, may go through similar identification disruptions in later life and then feel very deeply the pain of the earlier disruption. The interval between the first loss and the second similar one may have been generally tranquil. Faced with repetition of disruption of the identification instinct, however, the person may experience extreme anxiety, apparently out of proportion to the present threatened or actual loss.

After childhood, shifts of identification often occur at parturition, or following the death of an identificand, or the loss of a job, or the thwarting of creative effort, or extramarital infidelity. In addition, there are the unexpected illnesses or accidents. No instinct can proceed to maturity on a smooth uninterrupted course. These upheavals force a working out of a solution. The two dominant instincts are nearly always drawn closer together for the protection of the person involved, but not necessarily in a *mature* reconciliation. At such a time strong emotions prevail.

The first normal upheaval of instinct pattern comes with adolescence. Each "infatuation-identification" represents a working out of older identifications which are no longer appropriate or useful. If this natural development does not occur we see the spinster living on with her mother, the bachelor attached to his mother or her memory, and the man who so identifies his wife with his mother that he uses prostitutes as a release for his individuality drive in the sexual sphere. On the other hand, if an infatuation attachment leads to hasty marriage, individuality needs have in many cases been ignored, but will contribute to later resentment, infidelity, or separation. When divorce is carried through, a *maturing* identification instinct may permit a more satisfactory second union. Too often, however, such a person enters into a marriage relationship almost identical with the first, with all the problems unsolved and identifications caught at the same level of immaturity. Where there has been no true loosening of parental identification a young couple will frequently repeat the family pattern they profess to escape. The old childhood pattern of being like the parent in the parents' absence asserts itself. When the couple continue to live in a parental home, individuality rebellions lead to constant discord, especially where identifications with the parents still are binding.

A common statement is that love (identification) and hate (rejection of identification by individuality) seem so close together. This has created the impression that evidence of love *must* be counterbalanced by corresponding hate. In fact, however, such oscillations of love and hate toward the same identificand merely indicate that the two major instincts have been unable to cooperate in establishing a stable consistent relationship. Individuality and identification always work together, even in their most obvious antagonistic expression. Close examination reveals this mutual helpfulness despite surface appearances of violent dominance of one instinct over the other. It is understandable that neither one of these instincts should ever triumph over the other. Should this occur we face the horrifying picture of an Ophelia with *only* identifications to sustain her, or the alternative,—the criminal psychopath whose individuality does not know the discipline of an identification with normal human beings.

There must be some consideration of the special sensitivity of women to individuality-identification instinct function In association with the special physical role she plays in procreation, the mother of a new born experiences an unusually vigorous identification at parturition. This is a necessary condition for care of the new born, but the woman's role thus renders the female more susceptible to identifications than is the male. Dominance over her by her own instinct function do not characterize all of a woman's identifications, but her individuality instinct is generally more reactive against other outside controls. Her individuality must find a balancing freedom of expression. In this assertion, the female uses every device at her command,— home atmosphere; interest in and sometimes involvement with her husband's career; uniqueness in dress and coiffure. To be seen at a party in a gown identical with that worn by another woman is catastrophic because it diminishes the proof of her separate individuality. These same social occasions require that men dress exactly alike; the inner strength of man's individuality derives more from personal accomplishment than outer appearance.

Aberrant or immature forms of instinct development vary in intensity and manifestation from mild to extreme. An instinct may show mature development under most circumstances but regress to immaturity when faced with some old environmental pressure that remains unacceptable. The mild conditions are most often regarded as perplexing eccentricities. One example is the person who identifies so closely with a dead marital partner or relative that he or she develops identical physical symptoms. This phase of grief identification, with its insistence upon medical attention, is mystifying to other relatives but ordinarily subsides after some months. It is generally regarded as "nervous exhaustion" and occasions little overt comment. But a patient's more chronic, long-term identification with the deceased can become unbearable to relatives and close friends who have a feeling of anxiety and a desire to do the "right thing". Being human, they become angry through repeated frustration of their own efforts to deal in a direct fashion with the problems involved.

The basic causes of the more serious instinct disturbances (neuroses) remain unknown. Their manifestations suggest that one or both of the two major instincts of identification and individuality have failed to keep pace in their development with the chronological age of the person. Conflicts between these instincts, ordinarily resolved in childhood or adolescence, persist. Ease of shift in identification, typical of the teenager, continues so that the person seems perpetually unstable in his goals and personal attachments. Overt rebellion against a parent may be perpetuated through endless mistreatment of a marital partner. Because of constitutional factors and/or external circumstances the instincts of such persons seem frozen in the pattern of an earlier phase of life.

Disturbances of instinct function no doubt occur in the early years of life, although the author has not had the opportunity to examine them. It has been reported[10] that a child who identifies with a disturbed parent can himself present a similarly disturbed picture to the outside world, even with an appearance of psychosis. He may progress into delinquency or truancy depending to some degree, on the disturbance in the parent. An assertive aggressive parent who tries to dominate the family may clash with a child who is identifying with that parent and hence with his hostile behavior. The battle is endless; it moves in an unbroken circle. Later, identification in such a child may be directed toward a group leader who is disturbed and asocial, further perpetuating the child's imbalance of instinct function. In this case, individuality needs are merged into those of the leader and the satisfaction must be vicarious. Such projection does not lead to fulfillment; true individuality satisfactions must come largely from within the developing human being himself.

A converse situation can result in great harm. The youngster may attempt a complete rejection of identification with a parent who is either excessively ineffectual or domineering. He appears to establish his own standards of behavior,—usually extreme ones. On one hand he may obey no law but his own, defy authority in all forms, and appear psychopathic. On the other hand he may set up highly individual standards not based on practical experience, but rigid, perfectionistic, and impossible of attainment. Careful examination of both these extremes of reaction is worth a moment's digression.

The psychopath, or near-psychopath, is often violent in the assertion of his individuality; at the same time he frequently places himself in situations which both defy authority and yet bring him under the forcible domination of that authority. It appears that this type of person senses his own inability to set up self-regulation either by his own standards or by identification with parents or parental substitutes. He returns again and again to prison, apparently unable to function outside it. In his own unusual way he remains subject to outside authority without identifying with it, or by identifying with it in his highly individualistic fashion. If such a person survives to middle life he may progress to a point where his need for close contact with oppressive authority lessens and he is able to lead a reasonably productive life outside the walls.

At the other extreme, the person who sets up rigid standards of behavior by his own decision may drive himself to great achievement; yet rarely will he derive a sense of satisfaction from his own performance. His individuality instinct, which insisted on the rigid standards, finds them impossible of attainment. Conversely, the instinct for identification may be thwarted, since the satisfaction of identificands was not involved in the formation of his ideals and goals. Frankenstein, single-handed, creates a monster which gives him not satisfaction but torment. Release from these rigorous precepts is difficult or impossible. In later life the burdens of the person assumed in his ceaseless driving can often be shed only by semi-invalidism, alcoholism, or other illnesses. This condition of rigid perfectionism has many variants. In some cases the person has *apparently* made an early identification with an admired older person; in reality, he has identified with his own image of that person,—a distortion accomplished by his own individuality needs. Between the psychopath and the rigid perfectionist there is a whole gamut of less extreme disturbances of the instinct pattern, which confound the physician when he encounters them.

A common disturbance of instinct function may originate in part from insufficient association with the opposite sex. Then there is no opportunity for the normal infatuation process which would have freed the adolescent from his powerful identification with the parent of the opposite sex. In such a case the final choice of a marital partner is lopsidedly based on the dominance of one instinct (identification). If individuality later on tries to re-assert itself and reinitiate a search for a more appropriate life partner, the path is blocked by a choice aready made. Disorganized attempts at self-assertion in the marital situation may follow, —physical brutalities to the partner, extramarital affairs, derision, failure to fulfill sexual functions. In this situation, however, a break-up of the marriage is regarded as unthinkable by the belligerent partner; it represents a threat to an identification instinct trapped at the adolescent level. The marital battleground witnesses an endless oscillation of forays and retreats. A husband may constantly belittle and berate the wife when they are alone, and yet strive to appear a model husband to outsiders. This behavior duplicates that of the "impossible" child who behaves beautifully away from his home. The marital partner remains an identification substitute for a parent.

A father may develop extreme feelings of jealousy toward a new born child. He may be living or reliving an intense sibling rivalry. If he identifies his wife too strongly with his mother he will much more truly regard the child as a rival. Love for the newborn (identification) encounters the element of hate (rejection of identification by individuality).

# Some Cases in Point

Sickness, absence, and death of an identificand can force at least a temporary retreat of the individuality instinct. The instinct for identification, faced with painful loss, struggles to ensure the survival of the identificand. A 65 year old widow had lived for many years with a severely asthmatic husband and an equally asthmatic mother, both of whom dominated her. She was inseparably identified with both of them and, indeed, identified one with the other. The patient showed no clear-cut grief when the domineering and abusive husband died. A year later, however, when the mother died during an asthmatic attack an extraordinary change took place in the patient. A month after the death when she began to appear in public she astonished her friends. Instead of dressing neatly as before, she maintained a slovenly appearance,—she wore the bedraggled dresses her mother had worn; her hair became dirty and straggly; she assumed a distorted posture with rounded shoulders and bent back; she was seclusive; she complained of wheezing, excessive sputum and the need for large amounts of tissues to dispose of it. Physical examination, however, never substantiated these physical complaints. Her rheumatic heart disease, of which she never made mention, remained completely asymptomatic and well compensated. This striking resemblance to her mother persisted for 14 months during which time she was seen frequently for physical examination and discussion of her problems. No improvement was seen. Then one day, in a department store, she was about to try on the dress when her attention was riveted by her own reflection in the mirror. She was suddenly and fearfully aware of her present physical similarity to her mother and later told the author, "I looked in the mirror and there was my mother looking at me". The shock must have coincided with a time when she apparently had worked through a long but effective period of mourning for her mother. From this point on her physical complaints disappeared; she began to walk erect, wear her stylish wardrobe, visit the hairdresser, regain her vivacity of speech and spirit, and seek out old friends. She said, "I'm myself again". A careful review of this experience always brought her back to the incident in the department store,—her sudden awareness of her similarity to her mother, the fear that this meant she too was going to die, and the ensuing conviction that she would have to "fight back" in order to survive.

This type of instinct disturbance is the one most commonly seen by the physician. Although it has many variants it is always characterized by the survivor's strong identification with the dead person, an identification translated into the perpetuation of symptoms of the deceased, but with negative medical findings. The onset of this condition is somewhat obscured by the fact that the patient may not consult a physician during the first months when grief is at its most intense. It is probable that the intensity of the grief reaction forces the patient into a compromise that involves abandonment of individuality instinct satisfactions in favor of almost complete identification with the deceased. When the surviving identifier visits a physician he or she offers complaints similar to those of the deceased, wants similar treatment (even including operative procedures), and is convinced of impending death. Reassurance by the physician seems to fail completely. Despite this, the patient returns persistently, asking for help and refusing assurances of health. Such repeated visits must effect some measure of change for, after periods ranging from a few months to a few years, many such patients "learn to live with the problem" and function to better advantage. Some patients remain permanently attached to the physician as though he were taking the place of the dead identificand. Others

show an exaggerated continuance of the normally acceptable forms of mourning through frequent visits to the grave,
memorial services, and the permanent wearing of black
clothes, arm bands and widow's weeds.

Other unusual forms of identification-individuality imbalance are more difficult to recognize. Disturbance of the
identification instinct may occur prior to the death of an
identificand. The patient lives with a sense of impending
catastrophe and is forced into a type of premature mourning; he is excessively attentive to the identificand and not
uncommonly assumes many of the latter's symptoms. Yet
regardless of whether or not the actual death was prepared
for in this way the survivor invariably laments that some
decisive action might have been carried out, "if I had only
been there" at the last moment. If such preparatory atti-
tudes are successful the survivor's individuality instinct
needs to assume less guilt for old rebellions against the
identificand.

A 39 year old union executive had been an effective,
energetic, highly successful person until the birth of a
daughter who was found to have a hemorrhagic tendency.
Upon learning of this condition the patient developed
severe, frequent, and incapacitating episodes of faintness
and weakness which forced his retirement from work. His
wife had to assume the financial burden while the patient
took over the care of the child, was anxious to prevent even
minor injury to her, and summoned medical assistance on
the slightest provocation. The author learned, during his
association with the patient, that the latter had suffered
severe identification stresses in early life when his parents
were killed in an accident. This was followed shortly by the
illnesses and deaths of two uncles and an aunt with whom
he lived. The threatened death of his own child, with whom
he was very strongly identified, was sufficiently intolerable
so that he devoted all his efforts to preserving her life. In
this manner he prolonged the identification and eased his

sense of guilt at being responsible for her existence and suffering. The patient's symptoms suggested severe neurocirculatory asthenia similar to those of hemorrhagic shock that threatened the child. He constantly sought medical reassurance that he was not about to die and would be able to carry on with his domestic-parental duties; he never showed any interest in the cure of his symptoms or the possibility of returning to his former work. He refused to discuss the strong identifications with his parents, relatives, and daughter; he evaded this by prompt recourse to detailed, agonized accounts of his symptoms and general helplessness and by the expressed conviction that his own early death was inevitable. Remaining within the confines of his home and caring for the daughter seemed to represent protection for him. No change in his condition was observed during a long series of interviews.

A more severe problem may be suspected when a patient, strongly identified with another person, shows no grief at that person's death. Such failure of adjustment of identification, not involving a denial of death, may persist through many years during which the patient shows no sign of inner disturbance. Such an individual is in a particularly vulnerable state of instinct dysfunction; often a minor illness in another close identificand or serious accident to distant relatives may trigger most unexpected and bizarre behavior, including many symptom-complaints. There seems no explanation for the symptoms, mannerisms and dress of the patient; relatives and physician may be confused unless the emotional relationship to the earlier loss comes to light. This kind of postponed readjustment of identification instinct often has a chronic effect on behavior and is stubbornly resistant to intervention by family, friends or physician.

Extreme delay in the reorganization of the identification instinct was illustrated by a 53 year old single school teacher who, fifteen years earlier, had felt responsible for the death of her mother in a gas explosion. Despite an intense identification with the mother the patient showed little or no grief at the time, and said that others had commented on this lack of emotion. For the first ten years following this tragedy her behavior was apparently undisturbed. Five years prior to my observations she was found to have gall bladder disease, as had her mother for many years. After this diagnosis the patient underwent an abrupt and distressing distortion of behavior. On the one hand, after cholecystectomy she steadfastly refused to believe that she had the same illness from which her mother had suffered, and she spent the balance of her life in attempts to disprove the fact. On the other hand she reiterated symptoms and maintained a long-suffering attitude which coincided almost exactly with those of her dead mother. Individuality needs forced her to deny her rigid identification with her mother which she could not truly escape. She insisted that some obscure damage had been done her by her first and several subsequent operations, and yet was relentless in her demand for additional surgical operations in order to ascertain the cause of her alleged right upper quadrant pain. When the factor of identification with her mother was broached to this patient she became very disturbed and finally broke off contact with the author.

In this situation the physician should not face the patient with an explanation of his or her problem, nor hint that the patient is living out an old grief reaction in the grip of an identification instinct disturbance. The patient's individuality instinct will inevitably reject any awareness or acceptance of such dominance by the identification instinct over behavior. If such an explanation is attempted the patient will, at first, show astonishingly little interest in what the physician is saying. If the latter persists the patient will attempt to change the subject, become increasingly upset, and may even sever the professional relationship. The patient will continue to insist upon the organic seriousness of his symptoms despite all findings to the contrary. The physician must face this unpleasant fact:—Disturbances of instinct function do not yield to any *active* assistance on his part; he remains important, however, as a new supporting identificand.

Bereavement most often involves the death of an identificand older than the patient, but such is not always the case. Death of an offspring may disrupt the identification instinct in a parent. A dramatic example of this involved the father of a three year old child who had died of congenital heart disease. The patient felt intensely responsible for the death and, shortly afterwards, developed symptoms suggestive of cardiac disease. After continued medical reassurance failed to relieve the symptoms the problem yielded to a most interesting solution. The patient himself decided that he must engage in strenuous physical exercise the outcome of which would decide his fate. He began to saw down a large tree in his backyard expecting, at each stroke, to fall dead. After surviving the second-by-second agony of fear he felt a sudden release from guilt, and a strong sense of having been punished for any possible role in the child's death. Thereafter he was almost entirely free of cardiac symptoms and anxieties. This kind of abrupt reorganization of the instinct for identification may be accomplished because, simultaneously, the instinct for individuality is relieved of its burden of guilt by punishment. Several such episodes have been observed by the author in which complete identification with an identificand through death was violently imminent. Having "walked through the valley of the shadow" the patient can, at the same time, feel more closely identified with the deceased, and yet experience a loosening of that identification through the need for sheer physical survival and an identification with the real world. One outstanding instance of the above phenomenon was a middle-aged woman who was excessively identified with her rigid, domineering mother who had recently died.

Unable to loosen the identification by a normal mourning process she reversed her efforts and attempted to complete the identification by a suicide attempt. She had hypertension and suffered numerous episodes of paroxysmal auricular fibrillation. During one such episode she decided to end her life by rapidly climbing and descending twelve flights of stairs. She survived the near exhaustion of her effort and thereafter underwent a remarkable transformation which signalled the end of her intense identification with her mother. She promptly discarded many habits and mannerisms she had taken over from the mother, became freely communicative and energetic rather than outwardly dull and unsympathetic, and was able to show affection to her devoted but long suffering husband. The latter's comment was, "She's herself again". As might be expected, the patient showed little interest in discussing the reasons behind the change.

The persistent conflict between a strong identification and a strong individuality drive was illustrated by a 48 year old female patient. For many years this woman had ineffectively resisted domination by her mother-in-law, who was at the same time an unfailing source of emotional support. After the mother-in-law's death the patient expressed the expected anguish and grief at not being with the woman when she died. Her actions over the next three years showed the strength of ambivalent feelings arising from the identification-individuality conflict. On one hand she had energetically assumed the mother-in-law's responsibilities in the family business. At the same time she defeated this identification by a compulsive repetition of work that rendered her useless. When her husband developed hyperthyroidism and was faced with surgery the patient's energetic but unproductive activities were exacerbated. Her reliance on excess food and alcohol for relief of tension aroused the concern of her family. When the author attempted an explanation of the identification-individuality conflict as a causative factor the patient protested the idea vigorously and severed contact with the author.

Often a person caught in the struggle to break an identification under the pressure of individuality needs actually intensifies the identification in order to escape the pain involved in breaking it. A 27 year old fashion model had for years resisted strong domination by her physically handicapped father. In the course of one of their strenuous arguments the father suffered a myocardial infarction and died shortly thereafter. The patient then married a successful young businessman with whom she was very much in love. The differences in character between the two men were striking. The patient soon developed a contradictory and unpredictable pattern of behavior toward her husband. Without provocation, she would fly into rages designed to anger him and thus perpetuate the old relationship with her father; his refusal to respond in kind and thus reinforce her identification of the two men enraged her. On the other hand, when the goaded husband responded in kind she immediately rejected his response, as she had with her father. At other times the husband's violent reaction would arouse the patient's anxiety as though she were fearful that he too might be stricken and die. Then, for a time but not long, the patient would be docile and submissive. Since, however, the patient's marital choice seemed based primarily on firm individuality needs of her own the marriage was an enduring and even satisfactory one. A great many women have a need to "make over" a man based on their individual image of the "ideal" husband, but also colored by their identification of husband with father. Such a drive is frustrated not only by resistance on the part of the husband, but also by the woman's lingering individuality resistances toward her own father. In the above case the circumstances of the father's death intensified the identification and worsened the struggle.

A person may make a cross-identification of the marital

partner with a parent. A 54 year old policeman's wife cross-identified her husband and her dead mother, with whom she never had a mature identification. The patient's fears and apprehensions about her husband's death almost exactly repeated her previous fears for her mother, and seemed intensified by the death of her extremely ill daughter with whom she was also strongly identified. This focus of all identification upon her husband aroused a most natural fear of its disruption in the event of disaster to him. She was unable to tolerate any action of his which even vaguely involved a threat to his health or well-being, and was enraged at his refusal to be limited by her feelings of anxiety. Such overwhelming identification is always counteracted by inner individuality needs. Thus, in interviews she expressed resentment against his generally passive behavior; yet so strong was her identification need in this situation that she lived in constant fear of showing any overt resentment toward him. Loss of the mother and daughter had caused such painful disruptions of identification that she could not risk such an event again. The resulting inner struggle, frustrating and distressing, was not solved during the patient's contact with the author.

Death can have influence of another kind upon the identification instinct. A 29 year old personnel training executive showed a very unusual reaction which may have been a mild schizophrenic breakdown, though it was never clearly diagnosed as such. In World War II he had excelled in night fighting techniques and spent three years as an instructor in the art of silent killing. Nearly all of these activities involved attacks upon the victim's throat, in order to maintain silence. Late in the war he was assigned to an inexperienced infantry division which was decimated in the Battle of the Bulge. On the day of his capture by the Germans he was led before a firing squad six times, and six times "reprieved" at the last second. During the subsequent six months imprisonment he came near death by starvation, and survived only through the generous help of one fellow-soldier. Five years later, in a situation where he was responsible for the training of business personnel, he became extremely disturbed, and felt that outside forces over which he had no control were threatening him, his fiancee, and close relatives with whom he was identified strongly. He abruptly developed an agonizing fear of being strangled or choking, and was fearful of falling asleep at night since on frequent occasions he awakened struggling wildly against choking sensations. He found relief only through alcohol and by roaming the streets at night, napping briefly during the day. His harrowing experience before the firing squad and in prison camp seemed to have shifted his identification from attackers (the men whom he had trained) to victims (the decimated division, fellow-prisoners, family members whom he believed unfairly treated). In the civilian situation where he was again responsible for training others, his psychological breakdown found expression, in part, in the image of himself as a "victim" who was threatened nightly with garrotting and strangulation. During the subsequent four months of psychiatric hospitalization the patient showed no more obvious evidence of schizophrenic behavior, and eventually regained sufficient stability to return to work and family.

Many identification-individuality problems do not involve the element of death. Failure to mature one's identification with a parent produces a variety of behavior disturbances ranging from mild to severe. A young adult may be so identified with a parent that he feels forced to engage in the same occupational pursuits, and fulfill the ambitions of the parent rather than his own. This identification may be evident in an extraordinary attempt to live out the desires and ambitions of the parent. Then the besieged individuality instinct expresses itself in a variety of ways,— ineffectual outbursts of belligerence against the parent (except when the latter is ill and the recipient of great concern and sympathy), a domineering attitude toward wife, family, business associates, and subordinates. The inner turmoil can lead to physical symptoms, tension, sleeplessness, autonomic disturbances, extremes of physical activity, fatigue, variability of appetite, and attempts to relieve tension by alcohol or medication. Such a person may eventually consult a physician to seek reassurance that his health is not impaired. At the same time he obviously intends to continue the lonely struggle between the two instincts. Each person with such a problem must find his own modus vivendi. A solution that appears reasonable to outsiders may fail to satisfy the person's own instinct needs.

A young executive in business with his father had been entirely unable to make adequate identification adjustment to his father whom he considered rigid, puritanical, and domineering, and whom he defied by frequent bouts of alcoholism and secretive behavior. The family turmoil which these outbursts of individuality aroused resulted in numerous attempts to "reform" the young man; these he viewed as efforts to make him more like his father. After the patient left the family business and became associated with an older partner who was also an alcoholic, he abruptly abandoned alcohol and assumed his business responsibilities with vigor and resourcefulness. It is possible that he was able to become more like his own father only when separated from him, and when thrust into business and personal situations which resembled those of his father,— i.e., full responsibility for business affairs and for an inebriate business associate. The effect on his behavior can only be described as remarkably beneficial.

Sometimes a daughter is caught in a persistent identification with the ambitions and outstanding qualities of her father, especially where there is a strong similarity of intellectual talents and capacities between them. The father, sometimes disappointed in a son, may turn to this daughter, recognizing her potential of talents, and will try to encourage them, partly in an effort to further his own individuality ambitions and hopes. The daughter, though drawn by physical necessity and sexual instinct toward the feminine role, feels impelled to develop essentially masculine interests and talents. Such a patient consulted the author because of great concern about her heart, similar to her father's self-concern immediately prior to his sudden death. This young woman had taken over the role of the father in the parental home as sole financial support, decision maker, and devoted attendant upon the mother and, in the process, had fallen into the old family pattern of social seclusiveness. With such increased identification with the family, she was not able to undergo any maturation of instincts, with appropriate progression toward marriage and the establishment of her own home.

Rash individualistic rejection of parental identifications, without proper progression toward true maturity, can lead to disaster, often spectacularly. A female patient's refusal to be in any way like her dull prosaic immigrant mother found expression in an extravagant display of individuality, —the cultivation of unusual friends and marriage to an extremely talented man who, however, was ruined by alcohol and by contacts with the underworld. Despite a series of harrowing circumstances related to her husband, her children, and finally to her divorce, the patient persisted in her great need for individual expressiveness, finding partial fulfillment of it by writing a highly fanciful and stylized novel based upon her own life, and by continuing to idealize her husband's remarkable talents and personal charm in spite of the havoc they had wrought. Into very advanced years she continued to deny any advantage of identification with the "dull" and prosaic", and to hold persistently to individualistic standards of conduct as exemplified by her husband.

Strong expressions of individuality, however, can be tempered by suitable balancing identifications. A 21 year old male with severe rheumatic heart disease was violently rejecting of any identification with his mother, who had attempted a strong matriarchal role in his life. The rejection bordered on psychopathic behavior at times, but fortunately was tempered by a very close identification with his father, who was a gentler, less dominating person. After his marriage, however, the patient promptly identified both his wife and his mother-in-law with the rejected mother, and would treat them both in an arbitrary and .at times violent fashion. The identification with the gentler more understanding father seemed to keep the relationships in some reasonable balance until the patient's sudden death due to aortic insufficiency some years later.

Often what appears to be willful undisciplined behavior derives not from untrammelled individuality expression, but from identification with similar behavior in a parent. In such manner a pattern of illegitimacy may be established through several generations in a family. The illegitimate daughter lives out an identification with her mother by bearing an illegitimate offspring herself. Several such cases came under the author's observation. One adolescent girl, seen in a period of crisis, seemed compelled to follow out this type of identification in spite of every caution, warning, plea, and offer of help from many people around her. She herself expressed a conscious need to carry through this compulsion. An older sister, also illegitimate, to whom the patient was deeply devoted had recently died after long invalidism due to heart disease. In her grief, the patient expressed the identification-need to bring the dead sister back to life by herself giving life to another female child, preferably illegitimate like the dead sister.

A 36 year old female stenographer also illustrated the persisting pattern of illegitimacy. She knew of her own illegitimacy, yet seemed almost forced to live through her mother's role of unmarried parent. Just as her mother had done, she did not attempt to have her own pregnancy terminated, delivered the child, cared for it personally rather than placing it for adoption, and kept the matter secret by never marrying and by raising the child under an assumed name. The patient felt that she should never marry because the secret would then be revealed; yet she lived in fear that she would again let herself become involved with a man and repeat the whole pattern of illegitimacy. One fact of interest in such situations of illegitimacy is the excessive identification the illegitimate child may develop toward the single available parent. A more diffuse identification with two parents allows an easier loosening of parental identification in late childhood and adolescence.

Most identification problems are less spectacular. A 19 year old girl with rheumatic heart disease had been unable to grow beyond a child-like identification with both parents. Her heart disease was asymptomatic, but was a source of anxious concern to the mother. The patient's only expression of individuality toward the domineering mother was unrelenting passive resistance. Whereas the mother used words and constant nagging, the patient responded with silence and a refusal to express herself. In social contact with outsiders, however, she followed the mother's pattern of clinging insistence. Her silent resistance toward the mother was an identification with the behavior pattern of the father,—a passive frustrator who dealt with the vociferous, insistent mother by retiring behind his newspaper and ignoring her. With her physician the patient followed the mother's pattern of endless detailed ruminations about her anxieties, immediate feelings, and problems, —never yielding to any suggestion on how to handle them. The patient was not able to mature her identifications during a long series of interviews; when reinterviewed several years later, she showed no evidence of any progress. In situations where the identifier's physical illness has been a strong reinforcing factor in identifications, the identifications may never mature to the point where parents, so important to earlier security, can be relinquished

Very often young people, especially women, attempt to escape irksome identifications with family and parents by marrying at an early age, only to find that the new situation is repetitive of the old one. Often the young husband bears strong resemblance to the father, while the wife continues many strong identifications with her own mother. Then the wife begins to give vent to the old frustrations and resentments, which she now feels more strongly, against both home situations. She recognizes the similarities and finds herself caught in the trap from which she imagined she was about to escape. An important fact is worth noting. In spite of violent protests and shrewdish behavior toward the spouse, the young wife carefully evades the logical course of action, which is separation from the new situation. She cannot do this because she is too closely identified with, and therefore dependent upon, a pattern of life identical with the old familiar one which had given her security in the past. Her individuality finds no personal expression in this repetition of identifications except through vitriolic verbal blasts. She ruminates constantly over the situation with friends, her physician, her minister, or her psychiatrist, expressing criticism and complaints, but remaining unable to alter the identifications.

Old identifications may persist unchanged and immobilize a person in a distressing situation. A 45 year old patient with rheumatic heart disease had perpetuated a triangle relationship with her ex-husband and a male friend over a twenty-five year period. She had always identified her ex-husband with her strong, domineering father; the man whom she claimed to love, but could not bring herself to marry even after her divorce, had many of the more passive qualities of her mother. The patient had always resented her father's domination, and transferred this intense feeling to her husband whom she divorced in an impetuous outburst of rage. Individualistic as she was trying to be, she was unable to break the strong identification with father-husband, felt guilty and insecure about the divorce, and could not break off completely from the ex-husband by marrying the other man. The latter's passive qualities annoyed and enraged her, just as she had been annoyed at her mother's passive acceptance of domination by her father. She could cast neither man aside. The ex-husband continued to visit her regularly, ostensibly to see the children. The patient was in turmoil during these visits, yet was resentful and insecure when the ex-husband failed to appear. This patient was caught in perpetual rumination about her identifications; it seemed to be the only way in which she could deal with them. As long as she took no decisive step toward individualistic choices she could maintain the steady, though tumultuous, status quo. She constantly talked about "living my own life", yet her actions showed awareness that she could not trust her own individualistic impulses. She admitted to many mistakes in handling other people, especially her two grown daughters. One of these daughters was a real source of anxiety to the patient, who saw that the young girl was strongly identified with her and developing a similar pattern of behavior with the opposite sex. This situation proved clearly to the patient that all her protests and ruminations and efforts to "grow up" had been to no avail; the daughter was following the patient's pattern of persisting identifications which had never really matured. In this state of perpetual indecision she had many bouts of auricular tachycardia which subsided when she rather abruptly married the other man. Curiously enough, only four months after this seemingly decisive step, she died of pulmonary embolism during a bout of tachycardia.

An 18 year old female art student manifested a strong need to identify in every way with her mother who had been very close to the patient in earlier life, but who seemed recently to have rejected her. Her efforts to repeat the mother's life were astonishingly persistent and forceful.

When this fact was pointed out to her she vigorously denied it, as though feeling that her own individuality was threatened by such slavish imitation. In some contrasts, her artistic efforts, generally bohemian life, and refusal to acknowledge ordinarily accepted moral and social codes of behavior arose, not only from individuality needs, but from a thwarted identification with her eccentric father whom the mother had divorced when the patient was a small child. Her image of both parents seemed to come primarily from what she had been told in early childhood. She was closely identified with both maternal grandparents who had vigorously rejected the patient's father, possibly because they may have suspected him of homosexuality. The patient constantly provoked her grandparents' anger and rejection, as though closely identifying herself with the absent father whom she resembled in physical appearance, and whose place she had taken as a companion to the mother. As the patient reached adulthood, the mother rather abruptly turned away from her and married a man her own age, again fortifying the patient's identification with the previously rejected father. Accepting the grandparents' opinions, the patient visualized her father as a violent, unpredictable and completely unworthy person, and actually thought of herself in the same terms. In her associations with young men she tended to be associated with obviously homosexual or bisexual men with whose problems she became deeply involved. This may have been a reliving of the mother's similar situation with the father. Interestingly enough, this young woman was able to show some evidence of instinct maturation:—she established a brief but definite contact with her father, about whom she was able to develop a more realistic appraisal; was able to assume a more feminine, less domineering role, and eventually married, apparently satisfactorily. On one occasion this patient's mother expressed directly to the author her own unspoken thoughts about the young woman. With considerable anxiety she said, "My daughter is living my life all over again". The mother, however, seemed well aware that there was no effective way of preventing the daughter from living through experiences similar to her own.

A 34 year old housewife showed another commonly observed instinct conflict. Because of a close identification with her dead mother, whose domination she had resented greatly, the patient assumed the mother's role in almost every detail after the latter's death. She found herself being treated and used by her father and brothers, just as they had treated and used her mother. The patient raved and ranted against their attitude and behavior, threatened all kinds of dire action, and characteristically did nothing. She eventually married a man quite different from her father, as though in an individualistic need to make her own choice of marital partner. The husband, finding her unable to sever her close attachment to the parental family with himself only a new fixture in the old household, rebelled in a passive secretive way by gambling away all of his considerable earnings. Here was another male against whom the patient could righteously express rage and resentment, yet she consistently evaded any suggestion that she should assert her demands effectively. Her solution to the problem was one which she had seen to have been effective in her mother's handling of male oppression and resistance,—she became pregnant. By this relatively simple means, both in their minds and her own, she could now justifiably be relieved of her excessive responsibilities for the family's welfare. She was in a much better position to insist upon her own way or to demand that others be more considerate of her; yet, in spite of violent raging in repeated interviews, the patient could never make realistic demands on them. She was so bound by old identifications with the parental family that she could not risk the pain of a direct break with them, a fact which they apparently sensed and used to their advantage.

Identification with culture and environment exert an important control on human behavior. A person may wish to reject a culture because of his own individuality needs, yet cannot do so because his parents were strongly identified with it. A 19 year old female college student faced the problem of the second-generation American who is attempting to throw off identifications with the old world ways, faiths, and customs, but is still caught in an overwhelming identification with the parents and their struggles. The patient's individuality needs found expression in artistic endeavors of which the parents disapproved; her constant rebellions against parental restrictions and demands led to steady friction in the household. Although she dressed flamboyantly and generally contradicted the parents' rigid conservatism, the patient, in conversation, constantly defended them and their way of life, repeatedly pointed out her physical resemblances to them, lived out their ambitions for an education, and was attracted to young men whose religious interests matched those of her father. In spite of her rebellions and individuality needs, the patient expressed a belief that her fate was inseparable from that of her parents,—that no matter how loudly she rebelled, in the end she would have to pass down an almost identical road in life. This belief was reinforced by an extremely distressing experience when she tried to put her rebellion into action by consciously breaking a minor rule of her religious faith. This was immediately followed by violent headache and fear of death. In this circumstance she was found to have hypertension, which was known not to have been present shortly beforehand.

Rejection of identification with one parent is often accompanied by a great need to be punished for this rejection. A 51 year old female telephone operator had always rejected her mother as immoral, grasping, and completely avaricious. By contrast, the patient had insisted on playing the role of a hard working person always desirous of assuming responsibility, and unable to inflict injury or show dislike for anyone or anything. Such complete self-effacement may have been an effort to suppress her individuality instinct which persistently stirred guilt feelings within her through rejection of any identification with the mother. At the same time she lived in constant hope that her mother would eventually accept her again,—a hope that was not fulfilled during an illness and hospitalization of the patient which she thought might soften the mother's derogatory attitude. Instead, the mother called the hospital to find out if the patient had died and if the time had come to collect the life insurance. After such bitter evidence of continued rejection by the mother the patient adopted the mother's attitude toward her as a completely unworthy person whom anyone could justifiably scorn. Thereafter, she constantly placed herself in relatively degrading positions, dressed shabbily, was unkempt, sought menial tasks besides her regular work, and ceased rebelling against the verbal and physical abuse heaped on her by her half-blind and drunken husband. The patient spoke with some pride about the fact that "my husband kicks me around like a football", and never attempted to conceal her numerous contusions and extensive bruises. Guilt over the rejected identification with the mother may have been eased by such punishment; perhaps she was, in a way, identifying with the mother by enduring punishment which she felt the mother more properly deserved. In any event, this was the only solution which the patient found acceptable, and no amount of discussion or persuasion influenced her to change any part of her life. She never expressed resentment or intended retaliation against anyone who had inflicted physical brutalities upon her or had otherwise burdened her. The only effective medical assistance was maintaining her in a sufficiently ambulatory condition so that she could continue her regular job as a telephone operator.

A person caught in a strong identification can often protect himself by manipulating the identification which an identificand has for him. A 29 year old unmarried female could not bring herself to loosen her identification with her mother through interest in young men or marriage; she felt trapped and completely dominated. In this situation the patient developed headaches very similar to those of her mother who suffered from mild acromegaly. Whenever the patient felt unable to cope with the demands of her mother and other relatives, she resorted to a pattern of behavior almost identical with the mother's,—she fell back upon her headache symptom, which invariably subdued the rest of the family and eased their pressures on her. Despite her expressed ambitions in the business world, at last observation the patient seemed more secure in the continuing identification relationship with her mother, in which each of them was able to control the other by the use of their physical symptoms.

A strong identification need cannot be altered by a simple change of environmental circumstance. A 21 year old girl had been subject to repeated spontaneous fractures since early childhood due to polystotic fibrous dysplasia of bone. Her mother had constantly worried and hovered over her. The patient deeply resented this, felt intensely handicapped by her disability, was preoccupied with her social and sexual immaturities, and yet was intensely dependent upon the mother with whose anxious concern she had been closely identified. The patient tried to solve her problem by moving away from the family home but, in her new place of employment, immediately identified with an older nun who reportedly was anxious about the patient's physical condition, constantly fussed over her, and attempted to supervise the patient's personal and occupational activities. The patient's identification needs perpetuated this new situation, so much like the older maternal one, despite her verbal protests against it. Behind an overt rebellion and an apparently successful resolution of an old identification problem there may be found a shift of the problem to a new identificand. Though this offers only partial solution of the initial problem, it is some evidence of progress toward maturity.

# The Problem of the Prince

Any behavior theory worthy of serious consideration should assist the clarification of unusual as well as commonly observed examples of human behavior. Shakespeare's "Hamlet" presents a stern test of any theorist's cherished notions, since of all dramatic creations the character of the Prince has most persistently stirred speculation and as persistently defied definitive analysis. Madman, shrewd villain, ineffectual romantic, helpless victim—evidence can be offered to support each contention; yet by applying the yardstick of identification instinct, one can observe a logical progression in Shakespeare's development of Hamlet. Other characters in the play can be considered in the same light, where the dramatist permits us to do so. No such critique can be entirely empty of speculations, which however must respect common sense.

The opening of the play sets the theme—the power of the identification-instinct in controlling human behavior—by exploring certain facets of mourning for the dead. Death is the one irrevocable event which permanently disrupts an identification and thereby causes inescapable pain. The survivor responds most commonly by an initial denial of the death of the identificand; the deceased is referred to in the present tense and the events immediately preceding the death may be repeatedly reviewed and ruminated upon, as though by such effort time can be reversed and the event altered. Formerly, the ghost of the deceased was a widely accepted means of maintaining an identification with the dead person and the use of spirit mediums to revive the deceased has its believers today. Shakespeare singled out the resurrected ghost as a means not only of denial of death but also as a vehicle for communication of information and for confirmation of suspicions.

52

In the play, the soldiers of the royal household who were faithful to the recently dead king found the ghostly presence not unusual nor unexpected, and believed it an ill-omen. Horatio acknowledged the Ghost as representative of the king

"As thou art to thyself."

He too recognized the ill-omen of the Ghost, when he refered to the emotional disorder experienced by the Roman citizens at the time of the assassination of Julius Caeser.

"The graves stood tenantless and the sheeted dead
Did squeak and gibber in the Roman streets."

Such times of disordered feelings and reactivated mass-grief patterns related to old identifications are occasions of mob violence and public danger, such as may accompany abrupt change of high political leadership, particularly by assassination.

Horatio's decision to draw Hamlet into this grief-experience of communication-by-ghost triggered the subsequent chain of fateful events. The chief focus of the dramatist remained upon the disruptions of identifications which death occasioned, and the means taken by his characters to handle such identification problems.

The initial appearance of Hamlet himself emphasized the continuance of his grief, much beyond the ordinary duration of an acute mourning process. His persistent ruminations, as though thereby to keep the image of his father alive, suggested that some solution for his disturbed identification patterns would be one of the crucial conditions of the unfolding drama. Gertrude, his mother, suggested

"Do not forever with thy veiled lids
Seek for thy noble father in the dust.
Thou know 'tis common; all that live must die."
"Why seems it so particular with thee?"

Hamlet replies

"Seems, Madam! Nay, it is; I know not 'seems'."
"But I have that within which passes show;

These but the trappings and the suits of woe."
He made a clear statement of the strength of his identification with his father, when he considered reinforcing it through his own death.

"O that this too too solid flesh would melt,
Thaw, and dissolve itself into a dew!"
"How weary, stale, flat and unprofitable,
Seem to me all the uses of this world."
"An unweeded garden that grows to seed."

Feelings of admiration, love and hero-worship for the dead king mingled with feelings of strong rejection of the new king and of his own mother. His acute need for a solution of this grief problem left him vulnerable to any suggestion in this regard. Even before Horatio informed him of the Ghost, he said

"My father, methinks I see my father,
In my mind's eye."

Hamlet gave no indication of deeper resentments against his father, which would in any event be temporarily hidden beneath the strong grief reaction. Yet a moment's consideration must be given to the peculiar situation of interrelationships within a family which holds strong political power. The king represents a strong central authority with whom an entire group or nation may be strongly identified; for the king's son this strong cultural identification is superadded to the normally strong identification of son with father. In addition, the individuality of the young prince finds no outlet in pursuit of a life-work of his own choice nor often in the choice of a marital partner. His individuality may find expression in sporadic outbursts of wild and even antisocial behavior behind the scenes—activities which are tolerated by the family as long as the prince does not seriously reject his position and future responsibilities. Shakespeare did not dramatize this area of difficulty for Hamlet, but focussed upon the working-out of the grief-identification with the father.

The death of close identificands is often "blamed" by the grief-stricken survivor(s) on an evil act or error by someone close to the deceased. Hamlet interpreted the Ghost's appearance as indicative of foul play, just as Marcellus expressed the popularly held opinion,

"Something is rotten in the state of Denmark."

Foul play causing his father's death would justify an act of revenge, i.e., Hamlet could then take action to counteract the murder, even though he had not been able to forestall the original act. "If I had only been there" is an almost universal reaction to the death of a strong identificand; after the fact, however, revenge can substitute for that reaction.

At first sight of the Ghost, Hamlet was convinced and was able to communicate with it, since in the larger sense it was the extension of his own mental grief-experiences. The Ghost indicated that its tormented wanderings through the castle were punishment for

"the foul crimes done in my days of nature."

Hamlet's identification with the dead king's apparition was later obvious in his own similar mental and physical wanderings about the castle.

The Ghost's clear statement of Claudius' guilt satisfied Hamlet's inner need to blame someone for his father's death; and as his father's avenger, he found at last a definite direction in attempting to resolve the pain of the broken identification.

"Remember thee? Aye, thou poor Ghost, while memory holds a seat in this distracted globe. . . . I'll wipe away all trivial and fond records. . . . Thy commandment all alone shall live within the book and volume of my brain."

Shakespeare allowed no character other than Hamlet to establish verbal communication with the Ghost. The queen understandably was able neither to see nor hear the ghost of her dead husband—she had long since shifted her identification to her new husband, even before the king's murder.

The Ghost became not only unnecessary but for psychologic reasons an impossibility for her.

Hamlet's attitude toward "the groundlings who for the most part are capable of nothing but inexplicable dumb show and noise" may have been an expression of contempt for them but also for the common man's measures of expressing his emotions, related or not to grief and severed identifications. Yet he seized promptly upon the tradition of the ghost and identified with it, thus moving by primitive but effective instinctual means toward a solution of his identification-grief. When informed by Horatio of the appearance of the apparition, he accepted it immediately and without question, as a means of resolving and escaping the prolonged pain of his grief.

Hamlet's inaction and hesitation subsequent to his encounter with the Ghost marked a period of adjustment to the newly reinforced identification with his dead father. In this interval his behavior was disorderly and distracted, mimicking that of the Ghost. Ophelia's description of Hamlet's strange actions toward her, and his harried dishevelled appearance clearly confirmed his identification with the tormented dead father. The resolution of the grief process can, in an effort to solve the dilemma of a deeply disturbed and disrupted identification, pass through one or more phases of overtly bizarre behavior, often in an almost exact reliving of the dead person's experiences. Horatio and Marcellus were confused by Hamlet's speech and actions, as frequently occurs with relatives, close friends, or the physician of the bereaved person. Guildenstern's words

"by a crafty madness keeps aloof"

can be typical of a bereaved person's withdrawal from any attempts by others to learn the rationale of his bizarre actions. Hamlet did not expect others to understand their meaning.

"There are more things in heaven and in earth, Horatio
Than are dreamt of in your philosophy."

He did not wish his close associates to reveal the cause of his actions when

"I perchance hereafter shall think meet
to put an antic disposition on."

The playwright used dramatic license in allowing Hamlet verbally to reveal part of the meaning of his unusual actions to his friends; such usually does not occur in real life.

Both Claudius and Gertrude saw special meaning in Hamlet's actions but were uncertain; even Polonius observed

"Though this be madness yet there is method in't."

Still hesitant and confused as to the manner of completing his identification with his father, Hamlet in the famous soliloquy pondered on the favorable aspects of suicide as the most direct means toward that end and yet his ruminations over his own death indicated the conflict between the identification instinct (urging satisfaction through death) and the instinct for self preservation.

"Thus conscience does make cowards of us all,
And thus the native hue of resolution
Is sickled o'er with the pale cast of thought
And enterprises of great pith and moment
With this regard their currents turn awry,
And lose the name of action."

Other features of identification-instinct function are also evident. Hamlet's first contact with the players emphasized his identification of living persons of his own acquaintance with older fallen figures of Greek tragedy. In requesting the players to reenact the murder of Gonzago, with his own lines inserted, Hamlet clearly intended to use the power that the identification instinct exerts over an audience at a dramatic production.

"I have heard
That guilty creatures, sitting at a play
Have by the very cunning of the scene
Been struck so to the soul that presently
They have proclaimed their malefactions;

For murther, though it hath no tongue, will speak
With most miraculous organ. . . . . . .
The play's the thing,
Wherein I'll catch the conscience of the king."
Hamlet's rejection of Ophelia,
"Get thee to a nunnery. . . . ."
"Be thou chaste as ice, as pure as snow,
Thou shalt not escape calumny."

indicated his identification of her with his own mother. He
vented upon Ophelia the scorn, hate and contempt which
he could not as yet unleash against his own mother.

"I have heard of your paintings too, well enough. God
hath given you one face and you make yourselves
another. You jig, you amble, you lisp, you nickname
God's creatures, and make your wantonness your ignor-
ance."

He likewise showed open contempt for Polonius but his
hesitancy to attack other father-figures was evident when
he came upon Claudius at prayer and debated killing him.
He finally retreated, preferring (as he said) to kill Claudius
at the moment of some sinful act. In fact however his
strong identification with his own father prevented him
from raising his hand against any older man; his mistaken
slaying of Polonius resulted from rage and fear during his
tormented encounter with his mother, giving vent through
such action to the "passions" which he formerly detested in
the "groundlings." This moment was decisive, in that his
sword-thrust was intended for Claudius and it marked the
turning point in Hamlet from thoughts and words to action
at last. He evidenced little remorse for the slaying, though
he anticipated eventual punishment.

"Heaven hath pleased it so to punish me with this . . .
I will answer well the death I gave him."

This would be similar to the punishment which the Ghost
intimated had been visited upon Hamlet's father for his

"foul crimes" and in part for the killing of the elder Fortinbras.

At the time of his departure for England, Hamlet's major conflicts were no longer in evidence. He took upon himself the kingly prerogative of disposing of his enemies with cold treachery; no longer ruminating upon his own death, he moved directly toward it with fatalistic acceptance.

"There's a divinity that shapes our ends,
   Roughhew them how we will."

As he became the instrument of his father's revenge, Hamlet now would complete his father-identification through his own death. With perfect consistency he was now indifferent to the possible danger in the challenge to the final duel with Laertes, and he died by the poison of Claudius, just as his father had done.

Shakespeare did not present Hamlet's difficulty as a struggle between the individuality instinct and the instinct for identification. We do not perceive Hamlet as an individualistic human being—rather as a person completely caught in the grip of a grief-torn identification. We never clearly understand Gertrude. Claudius may have been impelled largely by a pathologic jealousy toward his brother as the ruling member of the royal household, though again his individual motives were not indicated. Polonius was the parent who under the guise of wise words attempts to maintain control over his offspring long beyond the period of ordinary parental guidance. He was so involved with his own personal identifications with his children that he seemed never to have suspected the facts of the king's murder, and preferred to function at the most shallow level of presumption — that Hamlet was disturbed because of Ophelia's refusal of him. Ophelia was represented as a constitutionally inadequate person, dependent almost exclusively upon her identification with her father as the sustaining force in her life. She remained submissive to him beyond the normal period of childhood dependency, showed almost no individuality strengths, and after Polonius' death became so badly disorganized that her suicidal reunion with her dead father was certainly the most easily predictable solution of her identification-disruption. Laertes was obviously less dependent upon Polonius and showed reasonable understanding of the need for youthful rebellion,

"Youth to itself rebels through none else near."

By contrast, the lowly gravedigger was the precis of individuality, being his own uninhibited man, envied by Hamlet—and the character in the play next after the Prince whom most actors enjoy portraying.

In summary, Hamlet was closely identified with his dead father, endured a period of intense mourning, and sought a new pattern of identification which might ease the pain of that grief. Early in the play, his reactions were the usual forms of grief, with intellectual preoccupation but no concrete action. Once clearly convinced of Claudius' guilt and having killed Polonius, Hamlet identified with his father through dimensions of violent action and kingly artifice, with disappearance of bizarre behavior and rumination. This identification involved a fatalistic committment and a final complete fulfillment through his own death. Such acceptance of death by the hero is a common theme in legend, religion, and literature; and the effect of death itself upon the survivors forms the basis of major elements in all tragedy.

# The Role of the Physician

In this day of concern for the "whole patient", and under constant pressure from well-intentioned sources to focus on "emotional" problems, the internist is left with a somewhat hazy self-image. His own experience tells him that the patients come to him for reassurance of physical well-being and correction of physical problems. For the most part they neither invite nor want interference in their personal psychologic problems: they do need strongly to identify with the physician and ask his help about such problems *as they see fit*. The physician's course must be shaped by his awareness of the fact that he can help the patient primarily through careful evaluation of the physical condition, interested follow-up, brief attention to psychologic stresses, minimal advice and, perhaps most importantly, a calm self-assured attitude with which the patient can identify.

The medical patient very often appears to be searching for a new identificand in his attempt to solve an identification-individuality problem. Many persons with such a need cannot use a physician as an identificand. There are other useful identificands,—ministers, lawyers, hairdressers, policemen, bartenders, social workers, nurses, sports and military heroes,—who often exert a stronger influence than the physician. Faith healers or astrologers may transmit more authority and have the capacity to fulfill the need. Some patients will go from one physician to another in endless succession, never able to resolve the underlying problem adequately. When a particular physician suitably meets the identification needs of a patient, the latter may become deeply committed to him; but in some cases there is direct evidence that a particular physician is actually adding to the problem.

A 39 year old female patient had a most distressing early

life within a very disorganized family, and eventually married a gambler who suffered with severe spondylitis. The patient instantly rejected the author as her physician, apparently on her almost immediate identification of him with her husband because of a close physical resemblance. This identification may have extended to a similar resemblance with her father whom she overtly rejected. The patient began to accuse the author of statements and implied meanings which had never been made at any time. She adamantly refused to consider any explanations or attempts at exploring the problem further, and expressed violent feelings far out of proportion to any immediate realities. This situation seemed to repeat her outpouring of feelings against her father whom she visualized as a threatening unstable figure; her husband, because of his illness, enjoyed protection from the violence of her feelings. The patient remained so resistant to "reason" and so unrelenting in her evaluation of alleged comments that she found a continuing professional relationship impossible.

In the presence of a strong attachment with a "faithful patient" the physician's understanding of the physical and emotional needs involved is invaluable. True, he very often can only watch and wait. Instincts are governors built in by Nature; they alter, if at all, very slowly. Since the instincts undergo alteration only through continuing life experience, the ruminations of a patient about his symptoms, difficulties, and emotional reactions do not in themselves alter the instincts, but are bridges toward the establishment of a closer identification with the physician or psychiatrist. By means of this new identification the patient hopes to steady his instinct pattern to the point where anguished conflict and inadequacies are lessened. That hope remains eternal even though its accomplishment is always slow, often incomplete, and invariably painful. For the physician, patience must be the handmaiden of understanding.

Involved in that understanding is an awareness of the

fact that a patient's attitude toward illness is greatly conditioned by how it affects instinct needs. If an illness is persistently viewed as an obstacle toward accomplishment of individuality satisfaction, then the illness is resented and frequently ignored, even to the point of serious harm. If, however, an illness tends to enhance the strength of identification with other people or suppress rebellious individuality in others, it may be most helpful and so is given up with great reluctance.

Verbal rebellions against oppressive figures with whom the patient is strongly identified must never be accepted as a definite prelude to definitive action or a "change of heart". The physician may agree openly with the patient's intentions; he should not personally expect effective action to ensue. There is a practical reason for this ambivalent attitude on the part of the patient. True rebellion is often risky. The domineering identificand may react so strongly to actual rebellion that any serious illness from which he suffers may be aggravated, even to the point of death. This the identifier cannot face. A person struggling with an identification problem may insist upon medical attention for an identificand, even when the latter's illness may be very minor. Thus the controlling force of the illness is deflected away from the identifier. By the same means the identifier, unable to face any painful dislocation of the identification, receives assurance emotionally, even though he may have known all along that the identificand's physical condition is not truly serious. Catastrophic illness most naturally will call for a shift of responsibility to trained medical personnel for purely medical reasons. This shift also fulfills the need of the identifier to know that "everything possible is being done" to prevent disruption of the identification.

The patient with emotional disturbance often seems arbitrary, unreasonable, child-like, shrewd, rigid, manipulating, and insistent that the physician "do something",—yet is completely resistant to any clarification of his problem. Not an easy combination of human traits with which to deal, yet inescapable. In attempting an explanation of such traits, the common case of the faithful long-suffering wife and the worthless drunken brutal husband may be useful. The term "masochistic" is impressive but hardly explanatory. Understanding the complex criss-cross of identification-individuality needs that afflict such a woman will make the physician at least more helpful to her, and comfortable with himself. Often such a woman was thwarted in the proper maturing of identification instinct because the father was an unsatisfactory identificand when she was a child. As a result she established an unusually intense identification with her mother, only to rebel against that as an adolescent. Her individuality needs probably sought expression through sharp criticism of the mother for the latter's handling of the father, that the mother was "responsible" for the father's behavior. The growing daughter, still seeking some way to identify effectively with the father, will often take on his point of view and be individualistically determined not to make the "same mistakes" as the mother. The immature identification instinct too often will be the determinant in the later choice of a marital partner in the dual need,

1) to fulfill identification with the father

and

2) to prove that she can "do better" than her mother in "making a new man" out of an unstable prospective husband.

Such a marriage, once contracted, seems astonishingly durable despite the husband's brutalities, desertions, infidelities and drunkenness. Even though the wife presents herself to a physician with physical complaints and evidence of physical cruelties inflicted, she remains loyal to the husband and often denies marital rift. Here is willingness to accept punishment for rebellion against the unnaturally strong maternal identification; here also is the persistent need to identify her husband with her father, and secretiveness to protect the individuality instinct against outside recognition of its failure to make a "new man" of the husband. Late in life, perhaps when time has allowed a maturing of instinct function, such a woman may change. Meanwhile, "reason" seems not to influence her. A physician should be wary of tears, bruises, and sudden "confessions" about the domestic situation. He can lend only a briefly sympathetic ear and bind up the lacerations, though in some way *entirely unknown to him* the patient's identification with him may be helping her instincts toward maturity.

Experience indicates that the instincts for identification and individuality do not tolerate easily either direct discussion of their nature or modification by intellectual means. It is characteristic of all human beings to have difficulty in making a good assessment of themselves or a clear estimate of those with whom they are closely identified. Our own individuality instinct will rebel strongly against our own internal assessment of ourselves. Conversely, a forceful continuing identification impels us to blunt all evaluations which are potentially destructive to our identificands. Where an identification has been willfully rejected a person finds the former identificand "all bad"; any softening of that attitude threatens the individuality instinct which is responsible for the rejection. Even if a medical physician has a reasonably good formulation of a patient's problem in terms of these instinct functions, generally he should withhold explanations from the patient. Faced with them, the patient invariably becomes restless, disinterested, evasive, disbelieving, tries to change the subject, may become tense and finally openly resistant to further discussion. No doubt all of us have degrees of unresolved conflict between identification and individuality instincts, areas of immaturity we can at least manage and do not wish stirred into action. Also, our strong individuality instinct resists any outside reminder that others control us by our identification with them; and that factors, as yet unknown, determine the growth of instincts and thus control us. Many people have an intense need to feel that they have themselves "under control" and fear any suggestion that factors outside their own control may suddenly erupt. This fear is realistic, and explains frequent visits to the physician who is believed to have great capacity to "control" many natural forces through his knowledge, his medications and his manual skill. Such belief on the part of a patient is a good stabilizing influence for him, even though the physician may privately be more realistic.

A great many medical patients actively resist any suggestion that even a small part of their problem may be psychological-emotional and will insist to the physician that physical-organic reasons are entirely responsible. In spite of his knowledge to the contrary, the physician is wiser not to struggle against the patient's formulation, but to offer reassurance on a physical basis only. When and if the patient is ready to disclose other aspects of his problem he will do so. Referral to a psychiatrist may be indicated and well intentioned by the physician, yet refused by the patient. If a patient's instinct function can permit new controls from outside and a shift of identification, then the establishment of a relationship to a psychiatrist will almost invariably be initiated by the patient. Short of clear cut psychosis in a patient which may force the physician into a more active role, the latter often can only watch and wait.

The patient determines his own course of action by his own evaluation of the problem. If he feels that it is "emotional" he identifies with a psychiatrist; if medical, with a physician. Very infrequently is there a shift from one orientation to the other. In one large university medical outpatient department[11] one hundred patients with significant emotional problems were referred to the psychiatric facility of the same hospital. A follow-up showed that the overwhelming majority so referred never kept the initial appointment, or returned to the medical clinic after two or three psychiatric consultations. The presence or absence of significant physical disease was not a factor. Only six patients were found who seemed to make an effective shift from medicine to psychiatry. In most of these cases the patient had initiated the request for change toward psychiatry after being reassured as to his physical status. A shift of identification from medical to psychiatric is not impossible, but should not be forced on a patient simply because emotional problems seem to be dominant. A suggestion about psychiatric referral may be made discretely but the final decision must rest with the patient.

A corollary of the above mentioned study suggests that the "emotional" problems of a psychiatrist's patients may have quite different emphases from those of patients seen by a medical physician, but this possibility needs further clarification. The psychiatrist and the internist appear to be faced with different sets of problems which need to be handled in different ways. Cross criticism is irresponsible and wasteful until each can see clearly the problems of the other's patients.

The bizarre behavior of certain patients requires added attention by the physician. A great deal of unusual behavior seems to stop short of psychotic breakdown and to be centered on the violent intensity of the struggle to meet the demands of the two seemingly antagonistic instincts of identification and individuality. This may lead to contradictory behavior and the patient is labeled schizoid or a "split personality". Many such people function well enough that commitment to an institution is avoidable, though they are withdrawn, ruminant, preoccupied with their physical symptoms, critical of inconsistency in others, and fearful of domination and "influence" from without. They seem to play different, often conflicting roles at different times. No serious problem arises for society until and unless the neurophysiologic mechanism of the person seems no longer capable of functioning under the violent stresses imposed upon it. The resulting breakdown may closely resemble schizophrenia, especially when the contradictory actions begin to occur *simultaneously* instead of at different times. A long period of medical and/or psychiatric observation may be necessary before a diagnosis of schizophrenia can be made or eliminated. In some cases the patient shows outward behavior and describes inner turmoil of such a nature that a clear diagnosis remains impossible.

# Other Aspects of Instinct Function in Human Behavior

A theory of behavioral instincts as outlined above, if valid in the medical context, must be equally applicable to human behavior in general; otherwise its soundness must be questioned. A brief review of several common behavior situations suggests a ready application of the theory to them.

Human activities are often characterized by an apparent predominance of one of the above-mentioned instincts over the other. A more careful examination, however, always shows that the supposedly less dominant instinct is finding a way to express itself in disguised form. Group life (crowds, mobs, teams, the military, the body politic, religions, nations, races, colors, business and social groups) can be considered from the standpoint of impressive identification features, yet through it the individual members achieve personal individuality goals which each might fail to attain on his own. Let us consider certain groups in this light.

A crowd may assemble, yet have few if any identification functions. People sunning themselves on a beach have little or no identification en masse; each is answering a personal desire. On the other hand, a crowd in a sports arena, while similarly fulfilling individuality wishes, has obvious and vociferous identifications. Most of them are identified with a particular team or player, suffering and exulting with them. Almost never does such a crowd have narrow identifications entirely in one direction. It will show approval of skill or good sportsmanship irrespective of the team or player involved. The groans, shrieks, and applause clearly demonstrate the depth of the identifications. Even though they be temporary they are deeply felt because, at the same

time, an area of individuality instinct is also finding satisfaction by a vicarious attachment to the contestants. This
represents a salutary balance of reasonably matured instincts and the result is a generally healthy expenditure of
energy, a loosening of tensions, and a shift away from the
daily routines. It is understandable that the adolescent, with
his groping for new identifications and his need for individuality expression, should be a most enthusiastic
member of such groups.

A mob shows these same instincts of identification and
individuality functioning toward a very different end. A
mob, as commonly understood, involves an identification of
*all* members with a particular purpose, most often as per-
sonified by a leader or small group of leaders. The assertion
of individuality by identification with a highly individualistic leader very often leads to defiance of a pre-existing
code of behavior. Momentarily, an older stable moral
identification is rejected, though ordinarily it will reassert
itself in the cold gray dawn of the morning. Very few people
can sustain a long-term identification-individuality pattern
of behavior involving violence, thievery, physical assault,
etc., if it violates codes established by earlier identifications.
Swept into rebellion against one identification by temporarily accepting a contrasting one the individual may commit
acts which would be impossible on his own initiative. The
downtrodden, the oppressed, and the deprived are likely to
seek individuality expression through mob action sanc-
tioned by the permissive custom-defying leader.

The military life involves a complex of identifications.
The instinct forces which knit together a military group
vary depending upon the tactical needs of the moment,
the type of leadership, and particular circumstances that
encourage a soldier's identification with his fellows. The
need to defend one's country in a war will involve identification with one's native land as well as identifications imposed by uniforms, drill, and community living of the

military organization. A vigorous competent leader, even when "disliked", is much easier to identify with than a weak vacillating one since the individuality-instinct need to consider oneself vigorous and competent is enhanced by such an identification. These broader identifications, however, would not be sufficient to sustain the combat soldier in the face of danger and privations if he had not established a close identification with his "outfit". For most soldiers this is the most important identification. It sustains him against danger, allows him to work efficiently under harrowing conditions, shifts his attention from himself to others so that he is not overwhelmed by the terror of annihilation, and allows him to make a choice of certain death for himself in exchange for the protection and preservation of others. Ironically enough, unusual acts of heroism are usually believed to be acts of extraordinary individuality based on exceptional inner traits. Many, perhaps most unusually brave deeds may be the immediate results of the need to preserve a close identification by saving the lives of identificands, or are acts committed in retaliation upon others for disrupting or threatening to disrupt such identifications.

Under pressure of combat the character of an "outfit" changes, as its original numbers are depleted by wounds, death, combat fatigue, transfers, and promotions. The hard core of original members have learned the tricks of staying alive; their identification with one another deepens with the repeated impact of danger; new members are grudgingly admitted to the inner circle; the majority of replacements are wounded, evacuated, killed, and in turn replaced. The loyalty-identifications of the "hard core", one to another, hold the unit together even though the pervasive identifications of the original unit, which persisted from boot-camp to battle, are not reestablished. Armies go on; within them the "outfits" come alive, mature, face danger, age, and die as identifications initiate, develop, and are disrupted.

It is not unexpected to find that the most efficient combat units are called teams, a term that indicates a small, highly organized, closely knit group of persons, each trained and skilled in his function, all with a clearly stated objective. The individuality need of each member is answered by his particular skill and function; his identification need is indicated by pride in his unit and attachment to his fellow-soldiers. An unusual military leader such as Napoleon Bonaparte might hold the identification loyalties of the common soldier by stirring his belief that he too carried a marshal's baton in his knapsack; but it seems likely that the capabilities of his men rested equally upon strong identifications with their immediate comrades in arms.

Politics is a very special area of identification-individuality instinct operation whose primary function is the choice of leaders and rulers who will, in turn, establish the rules governing the conduct of one person or group of persons toward one another. The choice of rulers is difficult at best, because it requires that the individuality instinct must submit some portion of its self-determination to the authority of another human being. Yet the forces which draw people together into groups, including the force of the identification instinct, necessitate some type of organized government, usually led by a single individual with whom the majority can make a reasonably satisfactory direct identification.

Some of the unease which stirs within a democratic state arises from the inability of the electorate to identify strongly with the rulers. Perhaps one reason for the success of the constitutional monarchy as seen in Great Britain is that the citizen can identify with a permanent symbol of authority while simultaneously voting for candidate and party of his own individual choice. The King remains the stable symbol of authority for long-term identification; the Prime Minister is the ruler chosen by the individualistic expression of the popular vote. In democracies, which lack the long-term ruler-identificand, the choice of Chief Executive and representatives in Congress frequently leaves unsatisfied the identification needs of a great number of the electorate. There is an acceptance of the *office* of the President as a symbol of authority, whether the President himself can be identified with or not. There is little or no strong popular identification with any ruler below the rank of President, excepting the leader of the partisan opposition. Times of crisis and danger, which threaten our self-preservation, call for increased identification with the ruler; peace and freedom permit an easing of this identification and greater opportunity for self-expression through criticism and even rejection of the same ruler. Rulers have been particular targets of assassination because of the violent individuality need of one person or group to reject the ruler's restraint upon them, or the restraint imposed by the social group in which they are living. "Uneasy lies the head . . ." because of the threat of an unpredictable rebellion of individuality instinct which can reject identification with the ruler only by destroying him.

An examination of different and differing political systems shows the universal need to strike an identification-individuality instinct balance.* Long-term identification with a strong central authority is not easily changed. Rejection of "l'etat, c'est moi" ruler identification by the people in the French Revolution was quickly replaced by a sweeping identification with Napoleon Bonaparte, so intense that it seemed almost a love affair. Overthrow of the czars in Russia was followed by restoration of rigid central authority as represented by Stalin and Politburo. The rejection of identification with established religion was counterbalanced by an excessive identification with dogmatic "religionistic" Marxist philosophy. When turbulent

*It is of interest to assess the United Nations organization with such an orientation of thought. Let two "enemies" spend sufficient time with each other to permit the beginnings of some identification between them and give proof that the individuality instinct of neither is truly threatened. Thereafter a more clear-headed intellectual assessment can be made.

readjustments of identifications are taking place there is often a negation of individuality needs; the people suspend rational judgment and accept a modus vivendi which satisfies the craving for a new supportive identification. When the crisis abates, individuality will reassert iself, usually through the rise of an articulate gregarious man-of-the-people leader who can lead by giving hope of individuality satisfaction as well as loosening of monolithic authority identifications. A dogmatic Mao was essential for newly-founded Chinese communism; a more liberal Khrushchev came to power in mid-century Russia. These two representatives of opposing instinct needs will necessarily show some evidence of conflict in their contacts, although Comrade Khrushchev would still support the identification structure of Communism against the more individualistically oriented West.

Another contrast between East and West lies in the apparent contradictions of philosophy and reality within each system. Communism insists that all men share equally; the people own all for the benefit of all. By such communal identification, individuality is submerged, except in the leader who must be extraordinarily vigorous and individualistic. In the West, where individuality has been permitted a maximum of development and permissiveness, the leader is not permitted to be as individualistic, but must be identified with a Party, is feared and disliked if he is too individualistic, and is curtailed in his exercise of power by a series of "checks and balances" and parliamentary delay.* Each type of leader is needed for the type of predominant political philosophy in each global area—and yet the type of leader will change as the instinct needs of the peoples involved undergo gradual change. It seems reasonable that deprivation and danger will draw groups

*While the political party as we know it requires a considerable identification of its members with the group, the "kingmakers" behind the scenes are, by contrast with the candidates, frequently remote from the public eye and handshake, self-determined, individualistic, acceding to public opinion and pressure only as expedient.

of people into more tightly bound, closely identified units which need aggressive individualistic leadership. When the hazards lessen, the long-suppressed individuality needs of the people begin to assert themselves in the direction of "private enterprise", private management of communal enterprises and the creative arts. In the past the opposition of political parties in the United States was based clearly upon these opposing instincts,—Republican individualism vs. Democratic group-welfare ideas of identification.

Political domination of any group will depend not only upon fortuitous external circumstances, but also upon the strength or weakness of recent individuality-identifications in the dominated.[12]Attempts abruptly to reorient those instincts by force are not likely to have lasting success. Slower reorientation, by prolonged military occupation and persistent indoctrination, may or may not succeed, depending to a great degree on how well the two factions intermingle and identify with each other. The much publicized "brainwashing" of individuals was a short-term, relatively crude effort at abrupt reorientation of identifications by cutting off all physical contact with old ones, and by intellectual attempts to discredit and replace them. "Brainwashing" may have been a temporarily successful tool of political expedience.[12] As a means of permanent political conversion it carries within itself the seeds of its own failure, when it tries to suppress all individuality needs and to destroy old identifications without adequate replacement. No human being can submit to this type of a double-barrelled attack and come out whole. The few successes achieved by the technique may have been due to the weakness of the identifications attacked and/or an inadequate individuality which allowed new identifications to be assimilated, especially under force.

In the adulation of certain public figures and personalities we again see this same interplay of instincts. There is a universal tendency to magnify individualistic deeds of accomplishment and, by identifying with them, expand our own sense of accomplishment or receive inspiration therefrom. We transform our doers of deeds into heroes; in the Golden Age we changed our heroes into gods. Mythology may be third-rate history, but it is an excellent index of man's need to alter truth to suit his individuality-identification needs. A hero may be villainous and survive if sufficient numbers of people can identify with him, especially if his villainy gives vicarious satisfaction to suppressed individuality drives. Jesse James is as much a folk hero as Daniel Boone; Billy the Kid even more so than Orville Wright. It is easiest to think of history in terms of the outstanding people who lived it rather than the numberless unknowns who truly made it possible. Even in this context we need an identification which takes us beyond the prosaic; in the process, history suffers distortion of truth which never finds correction.

There are obvious identifications with religious figures. The ramifications involved are so many and so complex that the author feels them to be beyond the scope of this book, and merely points up their existence for further contemplation by the reader. Identifications with own's own race, color or creed continue to defy legislation and education; identifications with native land and ideology are often stubbornly persistent. Change in these identifications is likely to occur only as a new generation replaces an older one.

Literature, drama and the creative arts are man's reinforcements of his identifications. The novels and plays with whose characters we can easily identify are the "good" ones. Although such identifications are temporary they bring into being emotions that add to the intensity of our own feeling of being alive. Beyond this private kind of identification, the performing arts allow the singling out of a few people as widely accepted identificands. The teenage "singer" with long hair and the cinema star whose acting ability may be marginal succeed because they offer a large section of the public a deeply rooted identification image. Because the identifications of adolescence are constantly shifting the juvenile idol of today is forgotten tomorrow. The continued popularity of a performer depends upon his maturing as an identificand while his admirers mature as individuals.

Even commercial enterprises depend to a significant degree upon the function of the two instincts under discussion. The success of the salesman varies according to the degree with which his prospect can identify with him. Sales campaigns and advertising reiterate the alleged superiority (individualism) of the product while striving to solidify the buyer's identification with it. Despite Madison Avenue, a person will buy or believe in the products which his identificands buy or believe in. This applies as much to the building of a medical practice as the promotion of a breakfast food.

# The Sexual Instinct

Any discussion of instincts must include a clear acknowledgement of the sexual instinct with its immense importance, not merely in procreation, but in many other areas of human behavior. The many psychologic changes and emotions arising from the sexual instinct have been detailed, discussed, and interpreted elsewhere:[2,13] there remains the need to put it in proper theoretical perspective, side by side with other behavioral instincts.

The sexual instinct, like the identification-individuality instincts, undergoes a progressive maturation from early life, through infant self-stimulation, childhood curiosities and anxieties, the latency period, puberty, adolescence, adult sexual activity, and eventual decline in interest and performance, with retreat of the instinct to infrequent expressions. Infant sexuality, stirred by self-stimulation and incidentally by the necessary manipulations of bathing and feeding, must, as the infant begins to differentiate the source of the stimulus, contribute greatly to increased consciousness of the self vs. the outside world. Later, especially in the male, sexual organs become areas of prideful accomplishment. The growing child, aware or not of the means used, is interested in the procreation of babies, their growth inside the mother, and often the sexual act itself. Early involvement of the child in sexual activity thus may stem not only from inner instinct drives but from an identification with parent activity.

The wane of sexual activity during the latency period is reinforced by the parents and by the strong identification with parental restrictions. As the child attempts to loosen this latter identification, his attempts to do so in the sexual area center in the telling of mildly obscene stories and jokes and a preoccupation with bodily functions. The development of the sex organs occasions both pleasure and guilt, pride in physical capacity (individuality) and fear of breaking childhood taboos (identification). Each developing child settles this problem in his own way, determined by the relative strength or weakness of the identification-individuality instincts as well as in terms of the force of the sexual needs, physical and instinctual.

Adolescence, with its strong awareness of sexual function, is often accompanied by an acute awareness of the separateness of each human being, an aloneness, and a knowledge of the immediate world about one as peculiar to oneself. The stirrings of the individuality instinct at this time are not easily explained, and may rest upon some central nervous system growth due to hormone change. In adolescence, when the identification-individuality complex is being so traumatically disrupted the sexual instinct may, indeed, play a very secondary role. This occurs despite undeniable physical sexual change. Many adolescents have a great need to deny its importance. Great amounts of energy may be diverted into other channels in the effort to master the surge of sexual force. Social and religious moral forces can be a self restraining adjunct. It is not uncommon for an adolescent to form a strong, primarily non-physical attachment for a member of the same sex. Most show free physical expression of affection for the parent of the opposite sex between the ages of thirteen and fifteen. These are most probably safety valves in the effort to prolong the latency period and deny change. This same type of semi-suppression may be observed a few years later during an early infatuation-identification. Sexual activity may be avoided then because the love object is idealized through identification with the parent. Other adolescents will indulge in sexual activity to further individuality drives. Whether or not this early indulgence accomplishes its purpose or results instead in a decrease in personal value is largely dependent on the social and cultural milieu in which the person functions. Masturbation may be the major sexual outlet during these years, though with the passage of time there will be recourse to more adult sexual behavior.

The gradual evolution of more mature sexual behavior may occur before or during the early years of marriage. Since sexual function, in the majority of adults, finds outlet in marriage the choice of a marital partner is especially important. The interweaving of instinct activity may easily lead to belief in the all-pervasive control of human behavior by one instinct whereas several are functioning simultaneously. Ideally, sexual function will increase the fulfillment of *both* individuality and identification needs. The degree to which it fails will affect the degree of marital strife or incompatibility. Although sexual skill may initially enhance the sense of self importance it will eventually, properly used, insure the strength of identification of one partner for the other. The sexual instinct is prominently emphasized by people as a vigorous facet of individuality—a sign of "manliness" or the "complete woman"—and through procreation leads to a host of identifications which exist in family life. The especially unique position of the sexual instinct is due directly to the fact that in its normal fulfillment one human being must relate closely to another human being. This obvious statement requires careful consideration, for in order to bring two people into close continuing contact there must be some degree of identification established one for the other. There must be a degree of submission of the individuality instinct to those of identification and sex. Herein lies the crux of so many marital problems.

Where the choice of a marital partner has been based primarily on a persistent unmatured identification with the parent of the opposite sex, the continuance of a "child-parent" relationship blocks attainment of full sexual maturity. If divorce or separation does not occur, a mistress or paramour may be used in an attempt to achieve some degree of sexual maturity.

On the other hand, a continued insistence by one marital partner on the use of sexual function to gratify his or her individuality needs alone can be a frequent cause of strife. For instance, A may have established a strong identification with B. B, on the other hand, while he may find temporary sexual satisfaction with A, has not been able to identify *maturely* with her and, in their relationship, constantly asserts an immature individuality instinct. Under these circumstances B cannot make the submissions required for a mutually satisfactory sexual relationship, and can go only part way in giving pleasure to A. If the instinct imbalance is an extreme one B deflects his sexual energies into other channels or may find satisfaction only with prostitutes over whom he can be dominant both physically and financially. The marital relationship itself may become an asexual one unless A is willing to be submissive, passive, and dominated entirely. Less extreme examples of this dominant-submissive relationship are common and sometimes work well, especially if the male, with his overt drive toward individuality, maintains dominance over the female, who tends more toward strong identifications natural to her maternal role.

Where individuality instinct is immaturely self assertive in both marital partners so that neither can really submit, then sexual activity becomes a battleground, an endless contest where true sexual enjoyment is denied to each by the other. This type of relationship may attain some degree of mutual satisfaction when an impressive show of resistant individuality is followed by the necessary "giving in". Such struggles are often accompanied by strong guilt feelings because, parallel with the immatured individuality instinct, there may be strong identification with the marital partner. In such cases there may be wide oscillations of behavior,—physical assault, assurances of affection, unkept promises to reform, etc. These feelings affect expression of the sexual instinct intensely.

It is astonishing how often a marriage survives its own asexuality because it is answering the basic needs of the identification-individuality complex. As instinct development occurs, this need to cling to one marital partner may fade and permit replacement by another. In this situation the sexual instinct has little influence. The sexual instinct, reinforcing the closeness of a marriage based upon adequately maturing identification-individuality instincts, improves the stability of marriage. Conversely, lack of sexual "compatibility" may hamper an otherwise reasonably good marriage, but not disrupt it where other instincts are adequately fulfilled. This situation is not comfortable but bearable, especially where some physical defect or aging process diminishes sexual capacity or interest. Decrease in sexual drive and capacity is a blow to the sense of individuality and may even shake an insufficiently developed identification. The usual decrease due to age involves a mutual waning of sexual interest, and so the problem will not be a major one if mutual identification has been strong during the preceding years between the marital partners.

The "fling at forty" may have many causes. Primarily, it seems to be an attempt to hold on to the earlier self-image, an individualistic need to strengthen identification with that self-image, and relive that earlier portion of sexually active life. In some instances it is an effort to live it for the first time. For many it is an abortive last attempt to escape a marital arrangement based too heavily upon parental identification; in middle life the individuality need for a freely-chosen life partner stirs anew long after the appropriate time for the search is past. Surprisingly enough, divorce and remarriage to a new partner at this time may work out well if the new choice is based upon *both* individuality and identification needs. Too often, however, the search is endless, with persistent philandering as a sign of brief infatuation-identifications more suitable to ado-lescence.

Sexual aberrations, both physiologic and mental, are well known though not always well accounted for. In consider-ing sexual aberrations it is difficult to separate the physio-logic from the psychologic and the influence of one instinct from another. Certainly, even after years of intensive study, the root of homosexuality is not understood. It remains for future study by more refined physiologic and chemical tech-niques to determine the possible organic substratum of this aberration. At present the problem remains unsolved, large-ly because of technological inadequacies. There is also the great resistance of many homosexuals to consider that this aberration may have an immutable organic character. It is easier to maintain the belief that it is "correctable" were the proper psychologic techniques used. For the homosexual who accepts his condition there is no problem in this area. For the man who had great need to identify with masculine forebears and whose individuality demands overall per-fection, resistance to the idea of an organic unchangeable cause will run strong. Similarly, rejection by the individu-ality instinct of identification with the mother and the feminine role will be strong in situations where there has been intense matriarchal domination. The homosexual tendency may thus tend to enhance and prolong the identi-fication-individuality antagonism.

A variety of other sexual aberrations certainly have their origin in immaturities of the sexual instinct, often in company with immaturity of the individuality-identifica-tion pattern. Voyeurism, fetishism, masturbation, sadism, and masochism are practices that give sexual satisfaction in a prolongation of immature habits of pleasure seeking.

# *Other Instincts*

It would be improper herein to discuss instincts which had not been the objects of my direct purposeful scrutiny, were it not for the fact that the workings of such instincts can hardly be ignored. Instincts function purposefully for the preservation of the individual and of the species, and with great frequency their operations overlap. The considerations expressed in this chapter have resulted from reflection only and lay no claim to scientific examination nor even to prolonged observation.

It seems reasonable to believe that there is within us all a strong force which insists that we protect and preserve our own physical entities. Even casual reflection suggests that the instinct for self preservation has had a most profound effect on the entire human race; but we can here put aside from our considerations the overt operations of that instinct, such as the acts of eating, fighting, killing rather than being killed, the organization of a protective society, the perpetual search for clothing and shelter, the development of agriculture and animal husbandry, the taking by force of productive lands, and the infant's shrill cry of hunger or fear. The special aspect of the instinct for self preservation which warrants careful thought is the fact that it is a powerful force which within each individual is eventually doomed to failure. Death, i.e., the termination of the physiologic activities of the body, must occur—yet for long periods of life the instinct operates as though this inevitability were not so. Such denial is most easily attained and most obviously successful during the younger decades of life, when "it can't happen to me" is a strong conviction and indeed a helpful one when it does not promote undue recklessness.

By the beginning of the fifth decade, however, the awareness of an approaching end to life begins to grow with considerable strength. Certain physical evidences of aging set in at that time and probably signal to the instinct for self preservation that a shift of attitude toward death is not only imminent but mandatory. Many active years of life still lie ahead, during which that shift of attitude can take place, often painfully at first, but in most cases gradually and without serious difficulty.

The instinct for self preservation secures material support from other instincts, especially those concerned with pro- creation, closeness to other people, and a strong sense of individual personal value. In greatest part, the instinct for self preservation depends upon the social institution of religion. The nearly universal presence of religion among men suggests a profound universal force within all or nearly all men. The emphasis in many religions upon worship of a First or Ultimate Creative Force has tended to overshadow religion's highly useful function for the individual human being, i.e., the assurance to the instinct for self preservation that the cessation of life-activities will not be a completely final event, that the human being's continuity will be pre- served by a variety of means. In some instances, such assur- ance has been so wholeheartedly sought and so forcefully supplied that the seekers willingly, even eagerly suffered death, their instinct for self preservation having been diverted from its genuine aim by an overwhelming identifi- cation with the religious experience. A congregation as well as a larger body of worshippers within a particular religion are bound by many ties of identification, often reinforced by the identification-values of a common ethnic background or national origin. Epic accounts of human experience, such as the Bible, assist in the assemblage of people into religions, through identification-values which focus on elements of behavior with which we can easily identify and through the perpetuation of the names and influence of long-dead human beings. Clear continuing evidence of the "immortali- zation" of our forefathers by such means and by the other

institutions of the social order offer support to the very vulnerable instinct for self preservation. To answer the need
that occasioned its existence, a religion must set up a pattern
of beliefs which support the concept of unending existence
in some form, if only in the memory of others; or at least
support the development of an accepting attitude toward
death, strengthened again by customs of ancestor worship
and by a code of living carefully structured to assure a maximum of personal satisfactions during life. Religion is the
rampart behind which the blind terror of the instinct for
self preservation can be minimized and mastered by the
majority of human beings. Within that rampart, logic and
reason wield little influence, as is true as well with the operations of other instincts. Religion shares this burden of illogic
with politics, the purpose of which is the self-preservation
of the social group.

To the small inquisitive child, religion offers a shield
between his urgent curiosity and the fact of his ultimate
death. We generally consider the small child's instinct for
self preservation too delicate to withstand an impersonal
confrontation with cosmic forces. For many, their childhood
confidence in religion lasts a lifetime; for others, at the time
of puberty and early adolescence, the broadening of the
educational experience and the rejection of many earlier
identifications brings the instinct for self preservation into
confrontation with a new set of values. And yet—life is
quick, vigor is at its peak, death is far off, so far into the
distant future that it can be comfortably ignored. This sense
of near-immortality, the youthful conviction of life's unending continuance loses its force gradually, sometimes abruptly
as the evidences of physical aging usher in the fifth decade
of life. The long period of years left after this realization in
middle life ordinarily permits a gradual acceptance of
approaching death, especially since the vigor of all instincts
and faculties gradually becomes blunted with increasing
age—even that of self preservation. Few aged people active-

ly seek death but they are progressively less troubled by its approach, being more and more isolated by the death of their identificands, and more accepting of the end of life as a release from the crippling progression of mental and physical infirmities. Many return their attention to religion in their waning years as a familiar comfort identified with their childhood.

To speak in detail of other instincts, without careful long-term observation, is to promote vague speculation. What do intellectual gratifications, music, human curiosity, mathematics, and humor indicate as to the presence of universal forces within us? A lifetime of study will be needed to answer each such question. We have hardly touched the surface of understanding ourselves.

# Some Final Thoughts

The *non-specific* manifestations of instinct function and dysfunction are the emotions. For purposes of this discussion emotions are defined as inner and outer manifestations of the satisfaction or frustration of an instinctual need. They do not, in themselves, constitute the solid core of so-called "emotional disturbance" as seen by the physician or psychiatrist. Nor do they indicate which instinct has been fulfilled or thwarted, but simply that some instinct function is or is not working well. Emotional turmoil is seen every day, yet it is difficult often to ascertain what brings forth its repeated, sometimes nearly constant display.

The *specific* dysfunctions of instincts, of which the non-specific emotions give warning, are:

1) Neurosis—Instinct function has not progressed or matured or kept pace with a person's chronological age, but is more appropriate to an earlier stage of life. The individuality needs of the neurotic are both insistent and immature. In an effort to satisfy them he often develops a highly refined skill in manipulating the reactions of other people for his own advantage. When his system of manipulation threatens to break down he seeks medical "assistance". Despite his insistence to the contrary, he does not primarily seek change within himself, but wishes to reestablish the status quo with the least possible rearrangement of instincts.[16] The neurotic "improves" in psychotherapy, very often not because of any inner change but because his "system" has resumed functioning to some measure of its former efficiency. We are far from any understanding of the cause for such stunted instinct growth; it may be both constitutional and environmental.

2) Psychopathy—The two instincts of individuality and identification fail to maintain any reasonable balance. One

seems hypertrophied beyond the capacity of the other to control it. Individuality is wildly excessive and uncontrolled, with a profoundly retarded capacity for identification. Conversely, we see the "constitutionally inadequate" person, unequal to the burdens of life and sustained only by dependencies and identifications. The cause of such imbalance is likewise unknown.

3) Psychosis—This is, most probably, a physical-chemical breakdown of neurologic function. General paresis,* traumatic injury, brain tumor, genetic defect and poisoning are the obvious physical-chemical disorders; schizophrenia and manic-depressive psychosis may well prove to be. It is interesting to consider the content of the latter two as they relate to identification-individuality instinct function. Whatever the cause or mode of operation of the basic disturbance, the *outer form* is clearly moulded by the instincts of individuality and identification.[17] Catatonic withdrawal signals a considerable break in the identification with the outer world; catatonic excitement, an extreme expression of individualistic need satisfaction. Hallucinations and delusions so often take the form of destructive criticism or malignant control from without,—a distorted parody of influential identifications, but reflecting their depth and vigor. The mentally disturbed patient's individuality instinct protests against the oppression with which these hallucinations threaten him. At the same time he protects his hallucinations since their destruction would disrupt his identifications. Delusions often include an extraordinary expression of individuality instinct: "The whole world" is against him; he is unique because of high achievement or because he is the "lowest" or the meanest. Conversely, through distorted identifications he completely merges with unique historical figures.

*The grandiose ideas of the paretic may indicate a loosening of restraints upon his individuality instinct, by destruction of his critical faculty and loss of contact with reality. His suspicions and paranoid delusions may represent a distorted awareness of his identifications, with their powerful control of his behavior.

In the light of these considerations it is understandable that behavior disturbances may at times be difficult to classify correctly. These disturbances show outward similarities because the same instinct functions which generally control human behavior are affected. Only the deeper and unknown causes of the disturbances differ.

Ability to control and manipulate the fundamental instincts will be the aim of research. To date, therapeutic investigation has produced striking effects upon *emotional* tone without altering the basic underlying instinct forces. The instinct for individuality seems susceptible to temporary chemical influence. Man has relied, for thousands of years, on two chemical agents—alcohol and opium alkaloids—to strengthen the individuality instinct. The chemical effect of alcohol produces a relaxation of muscle tension, an expanded sense of individual importance, and the ability to ignore responsibilities and pressures imposed by various identification forces. These effects would not account for the "need" to return to alcohol, once a thorough physical cure of the habit has been attained. This need may be an expression of the immatured individuality instinct's urge to bolster itself.

Western civilization is most familiar with the alcohol habit, though lately with narcotics also; the East, especially the Chinese culture, has faced the problem of narcotic addiction for centuries. The Chinese have been intensely involved with strong ancestor-identification in a rigid system of respect for ancestors, both immediate and remote, which tends to suppress adequate development of the instinct for individuality.[14] This may be a major reason for resort to chemical stimulation of that instinct, by the use of narcotics.

Other problems may be reexamined from this same viewpoint. Chemical and physical agents capable of strengthening individuality and identification might be useful in schizophrenia, in which these instincts appear badly disorganized. Whereas the schizophrenic seems to experience simultaneous contradictory function of these instincts at a primitive level, the manic depressive may be experiencing the same thing in more widely spaced phases and at a more sophisticated level. It would not be far afield to apply research findings on the individuality-identification pattern directly to management of the psychoses.

The discovery of any agent capable of altering instinct function would carry with it awesome moral implications and responsibilities. Research for harmful purposes is all too evident in the crudities of the "brain-washing" technique which is employed in the attempt to switch the victim's customary loyalties, based on identification, to new ones that will either neutralize him as an enemy or even utilize him to advantage. The so-called "war for men's minds", knowingly or unknowingly, revolves about instinct function.

# Epilogue

The purpose in setting forth these ideas is to bring order out of seeming chaos,—not to propose a final explanation, but to point a way. Any explanation of human behavior should fit closely the everyday facts and should offer reasons why human behavior often remains rigidly unchanged. There are many who will resist this formulation and these suggestions, not because they are newly set forth and differ from the principles of psychotherapy as it is now practiced, but because it is always difficult to admit the existence of forces within ourselves which seem to be beyond our own control. It is much easier to deal with the sexual instinct which seems, in part, under our voluntary control, or to "put the blame" on forces utterly beyond human reach. To learn that we contain within us forces over which we do not have complete control is most uncomfortable. This knowledge can be lived with if we realize that these forces have been built into us by the evolutionary process, and that they insure a high measure of stable behavior coupled with a huge measure of independence. We have only to recognize that they have a growth of their own which must be respected. Acceptance of this fact should bring us, ultimately, to a greater measure of personal maturity and inner peace.

# Bibliography

1. Grinker, R. R.—Archives of General Psychiatry 10:228-237, March 1964.

   Barton, R., Science and Psychiatry, Lancet, 2:566-568, 14 September 1963.

   Bixenstine, V. E., Empiricism in Latter-Day Behavioral Science, Science 145:464-467, 31 July 1964.

   Knox, S. C., A Decade of Progress in Psychiatry, Journal of the American Medical Association 187:959-960, 21 March 1964.

   Cowan, T. A., Decision Theory in Law, Science, and Technology, Science 140:1065, 7 June 1963.

2. Freud, Sigmund, Standard Edition, Complete Psychological Works, London, Hogarth Press, 1953.

   Wertham, F., Freud Now, Scientific American 181:50-54, October 1949.

3. Gesell, A. L., et al—The First Five Years of Life, New York, Harper and Bros., 1940.

   —The Child From Five to Ten, New York, Harper and Bros., 1946.

   —Youth: The Years from Ten to Sixteen, New York, Harper and Bros., 1956.

   Pollock, G. H., On Symbiosis and Symbiotic Neurosis, International Journal of Psychoanalysis 45:1-30, January 1964.

   Murphy, L. B., Some Aspects of The First Relationship, ibid. 45:31-43, January 1964.

   Greenson, R. R., The Struggle Against Identification, Journal of the American Psychoanalytic Association 2:200-217, 1954.

4. Webster's New International Dictionary, 2nd Edition, G. & C. Merriam Co.

   Brody, M. W., & Mahoney, V. P., Introjection, Identification, and Incorporation, International Journal of Psychoanalysis 45:57-63, January 1964.

   Watters, T. A., Identifications and Their Motivations, Diseases of the Nervous System 18:20-22, December 1957.

   Koff, R. H., A Definition of Identification: a Review of the Literature, International Journal of Psychoanalysis 42:362-370, 1961.

   Hart, H. H., Problems of Identification, Psychiatric Quarterly, 21:274-293, 1947.

   Meerloo, J. A. M., Living by Proxy, American Journal of Psychotherapy, 7:241-253, April 1953.

5. Lorenz, K. Z., King Solomon's Ring, New York, Thos. Y. Crowell Co., 1952.

   —Evolution of Behavior, Scientific American 199:67, December 1958.

   Hess, E. H., "Imprinting" in Animals, Scientific American 198:81, March 1958.

   Tyler, K. F., & al, Flocking of Domestic Chicks, Nature 201:108-109, 4 January 1964.

   Gray, P. H., Imprinting in Birds, Journal of Psychology 68:333-346, 1963.

6. Individual Tendencies in First Year of Life, in Problems of Infancy and Childhood, 6th Conference, Josiah Macy Jr. Foundation, New York, 1952.

   Thomas, Behavioral Individuality in Early Childhood, New York University Press, 1963.

7. Erikson, E. H., Identity and Life Cycle, Psychologic Issues, New York, International University Press, Vol. 1, #1, 1959.

8. Friedan, B., The Feminine Mystique, New York, W. W. Norton and Co., Inc., 1963.

9. Freud, Sigmund, Mourning and Melancholia, in Collected Papers, 4:152-170, London, Hogarth Press, 1925.

Pollock, G. H., Mourning and Adaptation, International Journal of Psychoanalysis 42:341-361, 1961.

Deutsch, H., Absence of Grief, Psychoanalytic Quarterly, 6:12-22, 1937.

10. Freud, Anna & Burlingham, E. T., War and Children, New York, Medical War Books, 1943.

11. Flynn, J. T., unpublished data.

12. Lifton, R. J., Thought Reform and The Psychology of Totalism, New York, W. W. Norton Co., Inc., 1963.

13. Various "schools" of psychoanalytic interpretation (Adler, Jung, Rank, Klein, Horney, Sullivan).

14. The Fate of Filial Piety, in Lifton, R. J., Thought Reform and the Psychology of Totalism, New York, W. W. Norton & Co., 1963.

15. Jackson, D. D., & Haley, J., Transference Revisited, Journal of Nervous and Mental Diseases, 137:363-371, October 1963.

16. Bergler, E., The Danger Neurotics Dread Most: Loss of the Basic Fallacy, Psychoanalytic Review 33:148-153, 1946.

Cohen, M. B., Countertransference and Anxiety, Psychiatry 15:231-243, August 1952.

17. Heimann, P., Defense Mechanisms in Paranoid States, International Journal of Psychoanalysis 33:208-213, 1952.

18. Munro, L., Clinical Notes on Internationalization and Identification, ibid. 33:132-143, 1952.